100
LITERACY
HOMEWORK
ACTIVITIES

- Stand-alone homework sheets
- Fits with any programme
- Easy to use

YEAR 6

Scottish Primary 7

Chris Webster

ACKNOWLEDGEMENTS

Published by Scholastic Ltd,
Villiers House,
Clarendon Avenue,
Leamington Spa,
Warwickshire CV32 5PR

© 2001 Scholastic Ltd
Text © Chris Webster 2001

Printed by Bell & Bain Ltd, Glasgow

1 2 3 4 5 6 7 8 9   6 7 8 9 0

AUTHOR
Chris Webster

EDITORIAL & DESIGN
Crystal Presentations Ltd

COVER DESIGN
Joy Monkhouse

ILLUSTRATORS
Ray and Corinne Burrows

British Library Cataloguing-in-Publication Data
A catalogue record for this book is available from the British Library.

ISBN 0-439-94486-4
ISBN 978-0439-94486-1

The publishers gratefully acknowledge permission to reproduce the following copyright material:

Alligator Books for the use of an extract 'Skylark' from *Junior Nature Guides: Birds* edited by Angela Royston, based on *Birds of North America* by Frank Shaw © 1995, Dragon's World Limited (1995, Dragon's World Limited).

Carlton Books Limited for the use of 'Very like a whale' by Ogden Nash from *Candy is Dandy: The Best of Ogden Nash* © 1959, Ogden Nash (1959, Dent).

Houghton Mifflin Co. for the use of 'Night Clouds' by Amy Lowell from *The Complete Poetical Works of Amy Lowell* © 1955, Houghton Mifflin Co. Copyright © renewed 1983 by Houghton Mifflin Co., Brinton P Roberts and G D'Angelot Belin, Esq. All rights reserved.

Ray Mather for the use of 'Two boys crying' by Ray Mather from *Scholastic Collections: Poetry* compiled by Wes Magee © 1991, Ray Mather (1991, Scholastic Limited).

Peters Fraser and Dunlop Group for the use of 'I'm just going out for a moment' by Michael Rosen from *Wouldn't you like to know* by Michael Rosen © 1977, Michael Rosen (1977, Andre Deutsch).

The Random House Group for the use of 'The Ecstatic' by C Day Lewis from *The Complete Poems of C Day Lewis* © 1992 in this edition The Estate of C Day Lewis (1992, Sinclair-Stevenson).

The Society of Authors as the literary representatives of the Estate of John Masefield for the use of 'Cargoes' by John Masefield from *Ballads and Poems* by John Masefield © 1910, John Masefield (1910, Elkin Mathews). Extracts from the National Literacy Strategy © Crown copyright. Reproduced under the terms of HMSO Guidance Note 8.

Every effort has been made to trace copyright holders and the publishers apologise for any omissions.

100 Literacy Homework Activities: Year 6

100 Literacy Homework Activities: Year 6

Using the books

The activities in each book are organised by term, then by word-, sentence- and text-level focus and, finally, by specific National Literacy Strategy objective. Each of the 100 homework activities is comprised of at least one photocopiable page to send home. Each sheet provides instructions for the child and a brief note to the helper (be that a parent, grandparent, neighbour or sibling), stating simply and clearly its purpose and suggesting support and/ or a further challenge to offer the child. Every sheet is clearly marked with a W (word), S (sentence) or T (text) symbol to designate its main focus. (Please note that 'they', 'them', 'their' has sometimes been used in the helper and teachers' notes to refer to 'child'. This avoids the 'he or she' construction.)

Making the most of these resources

The best way to use these homework resources is to use them flexibly, integrating them with a sequence of literacy sessions over a number of days. Such an approach will also ensure that the needs of an individual, or groups of children, are met in different ways. Some of the homework sheets will be greatly enhanced by enlarging them to A3 size as this provides children with more space in which to write. Others, for example, the sets of story cards, lend themselves to being laminated for reuse.

Here are some ideas for different types of use:

Preparation
- Give a word- or sentence-level homework activity to prepare for a skills session later in the week. This allows the skill to be reviewed in less time, thus leaving more time for group activities.
- Give a text-level homework activity as a way of preparing for more detailed work on a particular type of text in a future literacy lesson.
- Give work on a particular short text as preparation for further work on that text, or a related text, in a future lesson.

Follow-up
- Give a word- or sentence-level homework activity as a follow-up to a literacy lesson to provide more practice in a particular skill.
- Give a text-level homework activity as a creative way of responding to work done in a literacy lesson.
- Use one of the many short texts as a follow-up to a study of a similar type of text in a lesson.

Reinforcement
- Give selected word- or sentence-level homework to specific children who need extra practice.
- Give a text-level homework activity to specific children to reinforce text-level work done in class.
- Use a short text with specific children to reinforce work done on similar texts.

Supporting your helpers

The importance of involving parents in homework is generally acknowledged. For this reason, as well as the 'Dear Helper' note on each homework sheet, there is also a homework diary sheet on page 128 which can be photocopied and sent home with the homework. Multiple copies of these can be filed or stapled together to make a longer-term homework record. For each activity, there is space to record its title, the date on which it was sent home and spaces for responses to the work from the helper, the child and the teacher. The homework diary is intended to encourage home-school links, so that parents and carers know what is being taught and can make informed comments about their child's progress. It is also worth writing to parents and helpers, or holding a meeting, to discuss their role. This could include an explanation of how they can support their children's homework, for example, by:
- providing a space where the child can concentrate and has the necessary resources to hand;
- becoming actively involved by interpreting instructions, helping with problems, sharing reading and participating in the paired activities where required.

Discuss with them how much time you expect the child to spend on the homework. If, after that time, a child is stuck, or has not finished, then suggest to the parent/helper that they should not force the child to continue. Ask them to write an explanation and the teacher will give extra help the next day. However, if children are succeeding at the task and need more time, this can be allowed – but bear in mind that children need a varied and balanced home life!

It is worth discussing with parents what is meant by 'help' as they should be careful that they do not go as far as doing the homework for the child. Legitimate help will include sharing the reading of texts, helping to clarify problems, discussing possible answers, etc., but it is important that the child is at some stage left to do his or her best. The teacher can then form an accurate assessment of the child's strengths and weaknesses and provide suitable follow-up work.

Using the activities with the All New 100 Literacy Hours series

A cross-referenced grid has been provided (on pages 5, 6 and 7) for those who wish to use these homework activities with the corresponding *All New 100 Literacy Hours* book. The grid suggests if and where a homework task might fit within the context of the appropriate *All New 100 Literacy Hours* unit and there may be more than one appropriate activity. Sometimes, the homework page could be used for a skills session in class and one of the resources from *All New 100 Literacy Hours* can be used for homework.

PAGE	HOMEWORK TITLE	USE AS A FOLLOW ON TO:	NLS OBJECTIVE LINK	LINK TO 100 LITERACY HOURS
27	Spelling quiz	Revising basic spelling strategies	Y6 T1 W1	
28	Letter sequences	Finding patterns in words; how to use a dictionary	Y6 T1 W2	
29	Confused?	Adding suffixes to root words	Y6 T1 W4	
30	Building on roots	Adding prefixes and suffixes to root words	Y6 T1 W5	Unit 5 Hour 1
31	Connect it	Meanings and spellings of connectives	Y6 T1 W6	Unit 2 Hour 6
32	Can you speak Anglo-Saxon?	Comparing Anglo-Saxon words with equivalent words today	Y6 T1 W7	Unit 1 Hour 1
33	Sir Bedivere	How language changes over time with reference to archaic words, eg 'thee'	Y6 T1 W7	Unit 1 Hour 1
34	Place names	Researching the origin of place names	Y6 T1 W8	
35	Personal names	Researching the origin of personal names	Y6 T1 W8	
36	New words	Understanding how new words are made up	Y6 T1 W9	
37	Where in the world?	Using a dictionary to investigate etymology	Y6 T1 W10	Unit 4 Hour 4
38	Parts of speech circus	Revising parts of speech	Y6 T1 S1	Unit 1 Hour 4/5
39	The Great Eastern	Using notes to make sentences	Y6 T1 S1	Unit 4
40	Barbara Allan	Adapting a text for a different purpose and reader	Y6 T1 S1	Unit 1 Hour 3
41	In the future	Revising the future tense of verbs	Y6T1 S2	Unit 6 Hour 1
42	Active and passive	Changing active sentences to passive, and vice versa	Y6 T1 S2	Unit 6 Hour 1
43	Using connectives	Adding connectives to a passage of writing	Y6 T1 S4	Unit 2 Hour 6 Unit 5 Hour 3
44	Using conjunctions	Linking statements using conjunctions	Y6 T1 S4	Unit 2 Hour 1/2
45	Make it complex	Using conjunctions to form complex sentences	Y6 T1 S5	Unit 2 Hour 1 Unit 5 Hour 5
46	Note what follows	Using colons and semi-colons	Y6 T1 S6	Unit 3 Hour 2
47	Pop it in	Using punctuation to add additional information to sentences	Y6 T1 S6	Unit 3 Hour 2 Unit 4 Hour 1
48	The film of the book	Comparing a book and a film	Y6 T1 T1	Unit 3
49	Viewpoint	Looking at viewpoint in a novel	Y6 T1 T2	Unit 3 Hour 1
50	Little Blue Denim Jacket	Writing a modern retelling	Y6 T1 T6	Unit 3 Hour 2
51	Story planner	Planning the plot and structure of a story	Y6 T1 T7	Unit 2
52	Character cards	Planning characters for a story	Y6 T1 T7	Unit 2
53	Solar summary	Summarising a non-fiction text	Y6 T1 T8	Unit 4 Hour 2 Unit 5 Hour 4
54	From story to script	Rewriting a story as a playscript	Y6 T1 T9	Unit 3 Hour 4
55	Personification poems	Writing poems which use personification	Y6 T1 T10	Unit 1 Hour 5
56	Evaluating reports	Evaluating a report using given assessment criteria	Y6 T1 T12	Unit 4 Hour 1/4
57	Evaluating instructions	Evaluating instructions using given assessment criteria	Y6 T1 T12	
58	Biography frame	Using a writing frame to write a biography	Y6 T1 T14	Unit 5 Hour 5
59	Journalists' jargonator	Writing in the style of a journalist	Y6 T1 T16	Unit 4 Hour 3

PAGE	HOMEWORK TITLE	USE AS A FOLLOW ON TO:	NLS OBJECTIVE LINK	LINK TO 100 LITERACY HOURS
60	Suffixes plus	Sharing a text containing words with suffixes	Y6 T2 W3	
61	Number prefixes	Sharing a text containing words with number prefixes	Y6 T2 W4	
62	From curro to courier	Reading a text containing words derived from Latin roots	Y6 T2 W5	
63	All that glisters	Discussing a text which draws on proverbs	Y6 T2 W6	Unit 1 Hour 1
64	Past times	Investigating how words change over time	Y6 T2 W7	
65	Argument words	Preparing to write an argument or persuasive text	Y6 T2 W8	Unit 3 Hour 1
66	Active inventors	Considering the use of the passive voice	Y6 T2 S1	
67	Majestic trouble	Preparing to read formal/official language	Y6 T2 S2	Unit 5
68	Oily subjects	Analysing sentences in order to improve them	Y6 T2 S3	Unit 4 Hour 1
69	It's all relative	Writing more interesting sentences	Y6 T2 S3	Unit 4 Hour 1
70	Talk, talk	Writing dialogue	Y6 T2 S3	Unit 4 Hour 5
71	Dash it!	Reading a text containing dashes or hyphens	Y6 T2 S3	
72	Beowulf, folk hero	Preparing to write about a story or novel (blurbs; reviews)	Y6 T2 S4	Unit 2 Hour 1/2
73	Italy	Note-taking	Y6 T2 S4	Unit 3
74	Be an editor	Editing their own/another child's writing	Y6 T2 S4	Unit 5
75	If	Reading a text containing conditionals	Y6 T2 S5	Unit 3 Hour 2 Unit 5 Hour 1
76	School rules ok!	Reading a text containing modal verbs; studying verb tenses	Y6 T2 S5	
77	A Victorian vampire	Exploring paragraph and narrative structure	Y6 T2 T1	Unit 2 Hour 3/4/5
78	Alien paragraphs	Preparing for/following on from story writing	Y6 T2 T2	Unit 2 Hour 3 Unit 4 Hour 3
79	Venetian paragraphs	Writing or redrafting non-fiction	Y6 T2 T2	
80	You!	Considering poetic techniques	Y6 T2 T3	Unit 1
81	Cargoes	Considering poetic techniques/preparing to read a poem with evocative diction	Y6 T2 T3	Unit 1
82	Very like a Whale	Looking at simile and metaphor in poems	Y6 T2 T3	Unit 1
83	Swimming Swan	Reading humorous poetry	Y6 T2 T4	Unit 1
84	Two boys crying	Studying moods/feelings expressed in poetry	Y6 T2 T5	Unit 1
85	Introducing Claire	Developing character/crime or detective fiction	Y6 T2 T7	Unit 4 Hour 4
86	La Belle Dame Sans Merci	Becoming familiar with poets of the past	Y6 T2 T9	
87	Flashback planner	Planning a story	Y6 T2 T11	Unit 2 Hour 5
88	Crime cards	Preparing to write a crime/detective story	Y6 T2 T12	Unit 4 Hour 4 Unit 4 Hour 5
89	Television troubles	Preparing to write an argument	Y6 T2 T16	Unit 3
90	Dolly debate	Writing an argument	Y6 T2 T16	Unit 3
91	The directions game	Looking at instructions/imperatives	Y6 T2 T17	
92	How to argue	Planning a debate	Y6 T2 T18	Unit 3
93	Be controversial	Writing an argument	Y6 T2 T19	Unit 3 Hour 4

PAGE	HOMEWORK TITLE	USE AS A FOLLOW ON TO:	NLS OBJECTIVE LINK	LINK TO 100 LITERACY HOURS
94	Spelling guide	Focusing on tricky or difficult spelling	Y6 T3 W4	Unit 2 Hour 4
95	New word generator	Investigating how language changes	Y6 T3 W5	Unit 7 Hour 5
96	Word games	Fun and educational!	Y6 T3 W6	Any lesson
97	A handsome beast	Reading rhyming poetry	Y6 T3 W6	
98	As blind as a bat	Reading poetry containing similes	Y6 T3 W7	Unit 6 Hour 4
99	Your eyes are like	Developing imaginative expressions in poetry	Y6 T3 W7	Unit 4 Hour 3
100	Weregirl	Preparing to read or reading horror/other narrative types	Y6 T3 S1	Unit 1 Hour 1; Unit 5 Hour 3; Unit 5 Hour 5
101	Hengest	Studying recounts	Y6 T3 S1	Unit 3 Hour 3
102	Asteroid blaster	Preparing to read or write instructions	Y6 T3 S1	Unit 3 Hour 3
103	In the Atlantic	Preparing to read or write reports	Y6 T3 S1	Unit 3 Hour 1
104	The steam engine	Preparing to read or write explanations	Y6 T3 S1	Unit 3 Hour 1
105	Capital punishment	Preparing to read or write persuasive/discursive texts	Y6 T3 S1	Unit 3 Hour 2
106	Me and by girl	Preparing to investigate rhyming slang	Y6 T3 S2	
107	Mini-zapper	Looking at formal writing	Y6 T3 S3	Unit 7
108	Make it more complex!	Combining clauses	Y6 T3 S4	Unit 7 Hour 3; Unit 1 Hour 3 Unit 6 Hour 1
109	Hansel and Gretel	Practising complex sentences	Y6 T3 S4	Unit 6 Hour 1 Unit 1 Hour 3
110	Novel template	Reading a novel	Y6 T3 T1	Unit 5 Hour 5
111	Lost and found	Exploring two linked poems	Y6 T3 T2	Unit 4 Hour 1
112	Poet-o-meter	Studying several poems by the same poet	Y6 T3 T3	Unit 4
113	The schoolboy	Studying a sequence of poems by the same poet	Y6 T3 T4	Unit 4
114	Memorable Fancies	Reading several poems by William Blake	Y6 T3 T5	
115	Daphne and Britney	Comparing and contrasting two different forms of writing	Y6 T3 T6	Unit 2 Hour 5
116	Grimm's Beam	Comparing and contrasting fairy tales	Y6 T3 T6	
117	Night Clouds	Looking at figurative language in poems	Y6 T3 T7	Unit 4 Hour 4
118	Housecarle	Preparing to write chapter summaries	Y6 T3 T9	Unit 5 Hour 1
119	Design a book jacket	Responding to a novel/writing their own story	Y6 T3 T10	Unit 6 Hour 5
120	Book-o-meter	Writing a review after shared/guided reading of a book	Y6 T3 T11	Unit 5
121	Skylark	Reading poetry, to consider 'What is poetry?'	Y6 T3 T12	Unit 2 Hour 1
122/23	Fairy Tale Cards	Preparing to write a fairy tale	Y6 T3 T14	Unit 6
124	Spiders	Skimming and scanning for a research task	Y6 T3 T17/18	Unit 7 Hour 1
125	Cor!	Preparing to write a story/focusing on paragraphs	Y6 T3 T21	Unit 1 Hour 4
126	Euthanasia	Preparing to write a persuasion or argument	Y6 T3 T21	Unit 3 Hour 2
127	Form finder	Revising the appropriate genre for audience and purpose	Y6 T3 T22	Unit 3 Hour 5

Teachers' notes

p27 SPELLING QUIZ

Objective
Identify mis-spelt words in own writing; keep individual lists; learn to spell them. (Y6, T1, W1)

Lesson context
Any lesson in which basic spelling strategies are revised and/or practised – preferably near to the beginning of term.

Setting the homework
Ensure that all children know how to use the LOOK, COVER, WRITE, CHECK method of learning spellings and have a suitable book in which to collect words.

Differentiation
This quiz is for children at NC Level 3 (Scottish Level C) working towards Level 4 (Scottish Level D). Children below that level should have their spelling needs diagnosed directly by the teacher and given an appropriate list to learn.

Back at school
Weakness diagnosed by the quiz should be followed up.

p28 LETTER SEQUENCES

Objective
Use known spellings as a basis for spelling other words with similar patterns or related meanings. (Y6, T1, W2)

Lesson context
Reading a shared text which contains words with one or more of the letter sequences.

Setting the homework
Demonstrate how to find patterns in words and how to use a dictionary.

Differentiation
Less able children should investigate the first four letter sequences only. Because these sequences occur at the beginning of words, it is easier to find help in a dictionary.

Back at school
Using the board or a chart, share and collate the letter sequences which the children found during their investigations.

p29 CONFUSED?

Objective
Revise and extend work on spelling patterns for unstressed vowels in polysyllabic words. (Y6, T1, W4)

Lesson context
Reading a shared text which contains words with some of the confusing endings on the page.

Setting the homework
Explain about stressed and unstressed syllables. In every word, one syllable is emphasised – this syllable is said to be stressed, the other syllables are unstressed. Unstressed vowels are often pronounced with an UH sound which makes it difficult to guess the spelling.

Differentiation
This activity is designed for children at NC Level 3 (Scottish Level C) working towards Level 4 (Scottish Level D). Children below this level should be given an appropriate list of words to learn.

Back at school
Copy the cards onto an OHT and ask volunteers to put roots and endings together on the OHP screen.

p30 BUILDING ON ROOTS

Objective
Use word roots, prefixes and suffixes as a support for spelling. (Y6, T1, W5)

Lesson context
Reading a shared text which contains words with some of the roots used on the homework page.

Setting the homework
Revise the terms *root, prefix and suffix* and demonstrate how to complete the homework by giving an example.

Differentiation
Less able children should do the main activity only. More able children can investigate the additional roots.

Back at school
Share the words and meanings which the children generated.

p31 CONNECT IT

Objective
Investigate meanings and spellings of connectives. (Y6, T1, W6)

Lesson context
Use this resource as preparation or follow up to any type of comparative, evaluative or argumentative writing.

Setting the homework
Ensure that the children understand the term and have seen some examples of connectives in context.

Differentiation
Children who have not mastered nouns, verbs, adjectives and adverbs would be better doing a homework on these instead.

Back at school
Choose 10 of the more difficult connectives, eg 'consequently', 'eventually', for a follow-up spelling test. After the spelling test, revise the meanings of the connectives and how they can be used.

p32 CAN YOU SPEAK ANGLO-SAXON?

Objective
Understand how words and expressions have changed over time. (Y6, T1, W7)

Lesson context
Exploring the development of the English language and how language has changed.

Setting the homework
Explain that Anglo-Saxon was the language spoken by the Anglo-Saxon invaders in 449 AD. It is the ancestor of modern English and though, at first glance, it looks very different, it is possible to see the resemblance to modern English in many words.

Differentiation
All children should be able to attempt this page.

Back at school
Using an OHP, display a blank sheet and, in discussion with the children, complete the columns.

p33 SIR BEDIVERE

Objective
Understand how words and expressions have changed over time, eg old verb endings -st and -th and how some words have fallen out of use, eg yonder, thither. (Y6, T1. W7)

Lesson context
Reading any pre-twentieth century text, especially those of the 16th and 17th centuries.

Setting the homework
Discuss how language changes over time and explain the term archaic. Ask for examples of archaic words or terms, such as 'thou' and 'thee' for 'you'; 'goeth' for 'go'; 'espied' for 'spied'.

Differentiation
Less able children could be asked to focus on the first half of the passage only.

Back at school
Share the different translations of the Bedivere extract.

p34 PLACE NAMES

Objective
Research the origins of proper names, eg place names. (Y6, T1, W8)

Lesson context
Reading any text which contains several English place names.

Setting the homework
Use a map of Britain to show examples of the place-name elements. Suggest that a road atlas is detailed enough to show thousands of appropriate place names. Allocate specific counties to different children. Alternatively, supply copies of an appropriate map for children to use at home.

Differentiation
Give less able children a copy of a map of Yorkshire and ask them to focus on Anglo-Saxon and Scandinavian place-name elements.

Back at school
Share children's examples of place names. If they were allocated different counties, ask which place-name elements were the most common. Discuss what this shows (settlement patterns). If the school has internet access, the children could investigate the meaning of specific place names by visiting http://www.connections.ndirect.co.uk/pnames.html.

p35 PERSONAL NAMES

Objective
Research the origins of proper names, eg, personal names. (Y6, T1, W8)

Lesson context
A good preparation for any lesson in which children have to make up names for characters, eg writing a play or story. Note that page 52, 'Character cards', could be used with this homework, as it contains nine different characters.

Setting the homework
Explain that, for parents, choosing names for babies is very important and sometimes difficult. Authors have similar problems when trying to think of suitable names for their characters. This is an investigation of some sources of personal names.

Differentiation
None needed.

Back at school
Share favourite names and the names chosen for the characters. Did any children find out the meanings of the names they chose? Investigate personal names further by visiting http://www.behindthename.com.

p36 NEW WORDS

Objective
Understand how new words have been added to the language. (Y6, T1, W9)

Lesson context
Reading a shared text, probably an article or reference text, which deals with modern issues or products and, therefore, contains several new words.

Setting the homework
Explain that new words are continually being invented so that we can talk about new inventions and ideas.

Differentiation
Only the more able children should attempt the extension activity.

Back at school
Share the ideas from the 'Why We Need It' column and any other new words which the children have identified. Ask how many ways of making up new words they could find, eg from Latin and Greek roots, old words combined in new ways, old words used in new ways, humour, newly-invented words.

p37 WHERE IN THE WORLD?

Objective
Understand the function of the etymological dictionary. (Y6, T1, W10)

Lesson context
Use as a follow up to the shared reading of any text which contains some of the words on the activity page.

Setting the homework
Provide each child with an A3 size map of the world which shows the names of the major countries. If possible, lend children standard dictionaries and explain the etymological codes and the languages and countries to which they refer.

Differentiation
Only the more able children should do the extension activity.

Back at school
Share the world maps and any words from other countries which the children found. A good way to do this is to make a display of the maps and allow 10 minutes for the children to look at each other's maps and discuss them.

p38 PARTS OF SPEECH CIRCUS

Objective
Revise the different word classes. (Y6, T1, S1)

Lesson context
Use with a shared text and skills session which focuses on one or more parts of speech. Introduce this mnemonic poem early in the year and keep coming back to it throughout the year.

Setting the homework
In a question-and-answer session, find out what children know about parts of speech and reinforce that knowledge. Note that the children do not have to understand all the parts of speech at this point – the poem is part of the process of learning them.

Differentiation
Less able children can be given only part of the poem. The most able children will enjoy the challenge of the extension activity.

Back at school
Share the additional examples of parts of speech which the children have written. Ask for volunteers to recite the poem by heart.

p39 THE GREAT EASTERN

Objective
Re-express sentences in a different order – in the context of turning notes into finished text. (Y6, T1, S1)

Lesson context
Any lesson which uses the following process: 1) research using books, CD ROM etc., 2) making notes, 3) turning notes into sentences and paragraphs. The homework should be set between tasks 2 and 3.

Setting the homework
Write a few notes on the board and demonstrate the process.

Differentiation
Less able children could be asked to do tasks 1 and 2.

Back at school
Share the different versions of the final non-fiction texts and discuss the good and bad points. Apply the skill to a real research and writing task.

p40 BARBARA ALLAN

Objective
Adapt texts for particular readers and purposes. (Y6, T1, S1)

Lesson context
Responding to a shared text by adapting a passage. This homework is most effective when set as a preparatory exercise.

Setting the homework
Explain that the two main types of adaptation are: 1) Changes in form, eg from a ballad to a story, from a story to a musical. 2) Changes in language and style, eg into simpler language for children, into modern language for today's readers.

Differentiation
Less able children could adapt the first half of the ballad only. More able children could add descriptive detail.

Back at school
Share different versions of the adaptation. If time allows, produce a 'brainstormed' version on the board or OHP which includes the best features of several adaptations.

p41 IN THE FUTURE

Objective
Revise earlier work on verbs – future tense. (Y6, T1, S2)

Lesson context
Reading a shared text that contains several examples of the future tense, eg a prophecy, an article about the future, a scene from a story in which a character talks about his plans.

Setting the homework
Revise the word tense, recap briefly on the past and present tenses (both simple and continuous forms), add in more detail on the future tense using the examples on the homework page.

Differentiation
Less able children should concentrate on the writing task as they will use the future tense if writing about the future.

Back at school
Share what children wrote about the future. Choose some examples of future tense forms for further discussion.

p42 ACTIVE AND PASSIVE

Objective
Understand the terms *active* and *passive*; transform a sentence from active to passive and vice-versa. (Y6, T1, S2)

Lesson context
Reading a shared text that contains a high proportion of passive sentences.

Setting the homework
Explain the terms and find examples in the shared text. Spend a few minutes on verbal practice of transforming between active and passive.

Differentiation
Some less able children will fail to grasp the concept of active and passive. They should be set some simpler work on verbs. Abler children should attempt the extension activity.

Back at school
Go over the sentences verbally and ask the children to mark their own. Briefly discuss the difference in emphasis in some of the sentences.

p43 USING CONNECTIVES

Objective
Study how points are typically connected in different kinds of text: connectives. (Y6, T1, S4)

Lesson context
This homework is most effective when used as a preparatory exercise before a lesson that focuses on the use of connectives to link points, especially in argumentative/discursive writing.

Setting the homework
Revise earlier work on the spellings and meanings of connectives. Explain that this homework focuses on how to use connectives.

Differentiation
Many connectives are difficult in both spelling and meaning. Less able children should be instructed to complete the page with the help of an adult.

Back at school
Share the different connectives used to fill the gaps. Discuss the suggestions made by the children and choose the best suggestion to fill the gaps on an OHP of the homework page.

p44 USING CONJUNCTIONS

Objective
Study how points are typically connected in different kinds of text: conjunctions. (Y6, T1, S4)

Lesson context
Use as a follow-up to any lesson in which the focus has been on using conjunctions to move away from short sentences to longer complex sentences.

Setting the homework
Ensure that the children understand the term *conjunction*. You might wish to model the activity using an OHP.

Differentiation
The card game is easy enough for all children. Those of average and above average ability should also do the extension.

Back at school
Share some examples of statements joined by conjunctions and children's own sentences. If time allows, take the idea a step further by experimenting with joining three statements.

p45 MAKE IT COMPLEX

Objective
Form complex sentences by using different connecting devices. (Y6, T1, S5)

Lesson context
The page provides a summary of the main ways of connecting ideas in sentences. It is best used as preparation for a major piece of writing.

Setting the homework
Revise the main ways of connecting points. Experiment with different ways of connecting points.

Differentiation
All children should be able to use the first two methods. Average ability children could also try the phrase in apposition. The final method is for the most able.

Back at school
Experiment with complex sentences in the context of a piece of writing. For example, the children could be asked to write half a page on one of the following topics:
• Describe being part of a large crowd at an exciting event.
• Write a scene for a ghost story.
• Write an argument for or against one of the following:
  Christmas is too commercialised.
  All British police officers should carry a gun.

p46 NOTE WHAT FOLLOWS

Objective
Secure knowledge and understanding of more sophisticated punctuation marks: colon and semi-colon. (Y6, T1, S6)

Lesson context
This sheet focuses on the easiest and commonest uses of colons and semi-colons in complex lists. Use with a shared text that provides examples of this use of the colon and semi-colon.

Setting the homework
Emphasise that in a complex list the semi-colons are used to separate groups of items, while the items are separated by commas.

Differentiation
Less able children might attempt only the first task.

Back at school
Share answers to the tasks while the children mark their own.

p47 POP IT IN

Objective
Secure knowledge and understanding of more sophisticated punctuation marks: parenthetic commas, dashes, brackets. (Y6, T1, S6)

Lesson context
Shared reading of a text using commas, dashes and brackets for parenthetical information.

Setting the homework
Go over the explanation using an OHP, demonstrating the effects of different types of parenthetic punctuation.

Differentiation
Less able children might work with only one type of parenthetic punctuation, eg commas, using the first two sentences.

Back at school
Demonstrate why some choices are preferable to others, eg 1 and 2) commas are best as they don't make such an abrupt break in the sentence, 3 and 4) brackets are best because the extra information is more clearly separated – an 'optional extra', 5) dashes are best because the extra information is important and they make it stand out.

p48 THE FILM OF THE BOOK

Objective
Compare and evaluate a novel or play in print and the film/TV version. (Y6, T1, T1)

Lesson context
Any series of lessons which compare a book and a film. Note that this homework page should be distributed after the book is read. Collect it back and only redistribute it again once the film or TV version has been watched.

Setting the homework
Explain that the activity is in two parts, each to be completed on a different occasion.

Differentiation
More able children could be asked to use the headings, but to write more expansively on separate pages.

Back at school
Discuss and compare the different evaluations.

p49 VIEWPOINT

Objective
Take account of a viewpoint in a novel. (Y6, T1, T2)

Lesson context
Use before a lesson in which the viewpoint of a shared text will be investigated.

Setting the homework
Revise 1st, 2nd and 3rd person pronouns. Ensure that the children understand that the first person 'I' in a story can be the author (in an autobiographical story) or a 'persona'. A persona is an invented character who tells the story from his or her point of view using the pronouns 'I' and 'we'. In third-person stories, the author is narrator. Stories in the second person are rare, but include the 'adventure game' format.

Differentiation
Less able children could work with the first two texts only.

Back at school
Discuss the answers and follow this up with a discussion about the opportunities and limitations of each viewpoint.

p50 LITTLE BLUE DENIM JACKET

Objective
Manipulate narrative perspective by producing a modern retelling. (Y6, T1, T6)

Lesson context
Use with any traditional or archaic text as an example of how to retell a story.

Setting the homework
Discuss the different reasons for retelling a story: for example, to change the form (eg from a story to a play); to update it by using a modern setting; to challenge stereotypes (eg retelling a fairy story with a 'tough' princess).

Differentiation
Less able children could write the alternative ending, as the first part of the story gives them a model which they can follow.

Back at school
Share the different modern retellings.

p51 STORY PLANNER

Objective
Plan the plot and structure of narrative writing quickly and effectively. (Y6, T1, T7)

Lesson context
Use before a story-writing lesson.

Setting the homework
This planner focuses on different types of plot. After a while, children have experience of all the plot types. The planner can then be used to facilitate quick planning of future stories. Explain that children should write notes under the three main headings (Beginning, Middle and End) on the back of the planner, using the notes in the appropriate columns.

Differentiation
The plots on the planner have three levels of complexity. The simplest is the Problem plot, more difficult are the Quest and Flashback plots and the most difficult is to combine the basic plots with the other types of ending.

Back at school
Use the planning notes as the basis for shared, guided or independent story writing.

p52 CHARACTER CARDS

Objective
Plan the characters of narrative writing quickly and effectively. (Y6, T1, T7)

Lesson context
Use *before* a story-writing lesson for planning and *during* writing as a support for description. These cards are extremely versatile and can be used in several other contexts.

Setting the homework
Explain to the children that the first step is to think of a name for each character. Then, they should choose two contrasting characters as the basis for detailed character sketches.

Differentiation
Less able children could be asked to write one character sketch.

Back at school
Use the character sketches which the children have written as a basis for building up a story. The next step might be to develop the plot. See page 51, 'Story planner'.

p53 SOLAR SUMMARY

Objective
Summarise a passage in a specified number of words. (Y6, T1, T8)

Lesson context
Use before any lesson in which the skill of summary will be required, eg researching information.

Setting the homework
Revise the term *topic sentence*. The topic sentence states what the paragraph is about. It is usually the first sentence. Explain that the point of a summary is writing a shorter version by leaving out the less important points.

Differentiation
Less able children could be asked to do steps 1 and 2 and then write out the highlighted sentences in one continuous paragraph (this will be less than 150 words).

Back at school
Check the children's summaries. They should be one paragraph; they should include the most important points; no extra information should be added; they should be between 135 and 165 words.

p54 FROM STORY TO SCRIPT

Objective
Prepare a short section of a story as a script, eg using stage directions, location/setting. (Y6, T1, T9)

Lesson context
Reading a part or all of a story. The task is much easier if the story contains lots of dialogue, but more challenging and creative if it contains little dialogue. Children should have had previous experience of writing scripts.

Setting the homework
Make sure that the children understand the conventions of setting out a playscript by going over the example. Scene descriptions are brief and written in the present tense; character names are placed in the margin and are usually followed by a colon; speech marks are not used; stage directions are given in brackets (sometimes italics are used).

Differentiation
Less able children might do only as far as, "Quick, fetch a doctor." More able children could tackle the extension activity.

Back at school
Children in groups could act out the playscripts. Note that a playscript based on this story can be found in *100 Literacy Hours: Year 3*, pages 65 and 66.

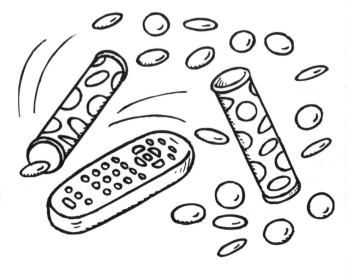

p55 PERSONIFICATION POEMS

Objective
Write poems experimenting with *active verbs* and *personification*. (Y6, T1, T10)

Lesson context
Studying figures of speech in poetry, specifically using a poem that makes extensive use of personification (eg Donne's 'Death be not proud').

Setting the homework
Explain that personification is describing things as though they have human qualities. For example, when Donne writes 'Death be not proud...', he is describing death with the human quality of pride.

Differentiation
Less able children may have difficulty with the term, but should use 'Storm' as a model for at least one personification poem.

Back at school
In future lessons, ask the children to look out for personification. When writing poetry, encourage them to use personification.

p56 EVALUATING REPORTS

Objective
Comment critically on the language, style and success of examples of non-fiction: reports. (Y6, T1, T12)

Lesson context
Reading a text in the report genre.

Setting the homework
Ask the children to find an example of report writing at home. This could be last year's school report or a consumer report or a magazine. The children should take home the text they read in class, just in case they can't find any suitable reports at home.

Differentiation
Less able children could deal with the simpler categories of Subject, Data and Conclusions and give a rating.

Back at school
Children could share their reports and say whether they agree or disagree with their partner's evaluation. A wall display of all the reports and evaluations could be made.

p57 EVALUATING INSTRUCTIONS

Objective
Comment critically on the language, style and success of examples of non-fiction: instruction manuals. (Y6, T1, T12)

Lesson context
Reading a text in the instruction genre.

Setting the homework
Ask the children to find an example of instructions at home. A photocopied example could be given if necessary. Ask the children to bring the completed evaluation sheet and the instructions to school the next day.

Differentiation
Less able children could deal with the simpler categories, Layout, Diagrams and Trouble-shooting and give a star rating.

Back at school
The children could share their instructions and evaluations. A wall display of instructions and evaluations could be made.

p58 BIOGRAPHY FRAME

Objective
Develop the skills of biographical and autobiographical writing. (Y6, T1, T14)

Lesson context
Researching and writing a biography.

Setting the homework
The children need to have completed the research process and have a series of notes ready to be written up into a biography.

Differentiation
Less able children should write directly on the writing frame. Average ability children should write on paper but follow the paragraph plan. More able children should be encouraged to adapt and extend the paragraph plan.

Back at school
Share the biographies. This is most effective when children have chosen different subjects about which to research and write.

p59 JOURNALIST'S JARGONATOR

Objective
Use the styles and conventions of journalism to report on real or imagined events. (Y6, T1, T16)

Lesson context
Writing in the style of a newspaper. This homework is most effective when used before the lesson as a preparatory exercise.

Setting the homework
Explain how to use the 'Journalist's Jargonator' by discussing 'before' and 'after' examples on the page.

Differentiation
Less able children could use the easier words and phrases from the first column of each box only.

Back at school
Divide the class into groups of 6–8. Each group should pool its articles and write a composite newsletter. Share and discuss the group newsletters.

TERM 2

p60 SUFFIXES PLUS

Objective
Use independent spelling strategies by applying knowledge of spelling rules: adding suffixes.(Y6, T2, W3)

Lesson context
Reading a shared text in which there are several examples of words with the suffixes listed in column 2.

Setting the homework
Check that the children understand the term *suffix*, revise the spelling rules cited on the homework page and give some examples.

Differentiation
Less able children could work with the first 10 words only. More able children could be asked to find more examples of words ending with the suffixes in column 2.

Back at school
Children could work in pairs to check that they have applied the rules correctly while the teacher provides support.

p61 NUMBER PREFIXES

Objective
Revise and consolidate work from previous terms: number prefixes. (Y6, T2, W4)

Lesson context
Reading a shared text in which there are several examples of words which begin with number prefixes.

Setting the homework
Check that the children understand the term *prefix*. Explain that when they think they have found a suitable word, they must ask themselves whether it suggests a number. This will enable them to reject words which begin with the same letters but are not number prefixes, eg biology, bite.

Differentiation
Less able children could work with uni-, bi- and tri- only. More able children could tackle the extension task.

Back at school
Read out and discuss the words and make a class list of words with number prefixes. Add to this during the term.

p62 FROM CURRO TO COURIER

Objective
Extend work on word origins: Latin roots. (Y6, T2, W5)

Lesson context
Use with a text in which there are several examples of words which derive from Latin roots. Alternatively, use in the context of a study of the origins of the English language.

Setting the homework
Remind the children that Latin was spoken by the Romans and has had a big influence on modern English. Explain that the homework is a matching exercise, using the example 'curro' and 'courier' on the page.

Differentiation
Less able children could be asked to make any ten matches. The more able children could be asked to tackle the extension task.

Back at school
Check the homework as a class activity. Additional Latin roots the children might find modern words for are: *clamo* – shout; *teneo* – hold; *vanus* – empty; *voco* – call.

p63 ALL THAT GLISTERS

Objective
Collect and explain the meaning and origins of proverbs. (Y6, T2, W6)

Lesson context
Use as a follow-up to a folk tale based on a proverb and/or as preparation for writing a short story which illustrates a proverb.

Setting the homework
Explain that a proverb is a piece of folk wisdom expressed in a memorable saying, to teach a lesson. Brainstorm examples and demonstrate how to explain them. An example is given.

Differentiation
Less able children should give the meanings of any four proverbs. All children can be encouraged to find more proverbs.

Back at school
Discuss the meanings of the proverbs and share the other proverbs which the children identified. Discuss what can be learned about life from proverbs. Write a short story which illustrates a proverb.

p64 PAST TIMES

Objective
Understand that the meaning of words changes over time. (Y6, T2, W7)

Lesson context
This homework is most effective when used in the context of a language investigation into aspects of the development of the English language.

Setting the homework
Remind the children that the meaning of words can change over time and that they will be exploring some examples. Explain that they should try out some of the words with their original meanings in the form of a newspaper article.

Differentiation
Abler pupils only could be asked to tackle the extension activity which is a demanding research task.

Back at school
Children will enjoy hearing each others' newspaper articles. Children who were able to find out more word histories should read and discuss them with the class.

p65 ARGUMENT WORDS

Objective
Build a bank of useful terms and phrases for argument.
(Y6, T2, W8)

Lesson context
Preparing for a piece of argumentative or persuasive writing.

Setting the homework
Explain that arguments, especially written arguments, use a range of words and phrases to compare and contrast ideas, some of which are quite difficult.

Differentiation
This homework page is most appropriate for more able children. Less able children could be given page 31, 'Connect it' and average ability children could be given page 43, 'Using connectives' (both from Term 1). All three sheets offer the opportunity to work with words which are helpful in creating arguments.

Back at school
Further preparation may follow, eg by using a resource, such as page 92, 'How to argue', or by practising argument orally. Ultimately, this preparatory work would lead to the writing of an argumentative or persuasive essay.

p66 ACTIVE INVENTORS

Objective
Investigate further the use of active and passive verbs. (Y6, T2, S1)

Lesson context
Use as a follow-up to reading, particularly of non-fiction texts in which the passive voice has been extensively used, or as a preparation for non-fiction writing.

Setting the homework
Revise the active and passive voice and how to change between them (see page 42, 'Active and passive'). Use the examples on the sheet to explain what to do.

Differentiation
Children who are still unsure about the difference between active and passive could do page 42, 'Active and passive' (Term 1) instead. More able children could be asked to tackle the extension task.

Back at school
Ask the children to share the sentences they have written.

p67 MAJESTIC TROUBLE

Objective
Understand formal, official language by analysing examples. (Y6, T2, S2)

Lesson context
Use as a preparation for reading other examples of formal, official language, or as part of an investigation into language variety or register.

Setting the homework
Explain to the children that the 'Notice' is a good example of the kind of official language that they will face in adult life.

Differentiation
Most children should concentrate on the main activity, finding out the meanings of words they do not understand. More able children can be asked to tackle the extension task.

Back at school
Go over some of the difficult words, eg 'pursuant', 'procedure' and 'restitution'; then ask the children for the answers to the questions. Finally, read out and discuss any other examples.

p68 OILY SUBJECTS

Objective
Revise work on complex sentences: identifying main clauses – finding the subject of a sentence. (Y6, T2, S3)

Lesson context
Teaching the children how to build longer and more interesting sentences.

Setting the homework
Explain to the children that it is sometimes necessary to analyse sentences to find a mistake or to find the best way to change or extend them. The first step in analysing a sentence is to find the main verb and subject. Take the children through the three-step method of doing this, described on the homework sheet.

Differentiation
Most children should be able to do at least the first three sentences. Sentences 4–8 are more difficult. You could adapt them before giving the activity to some children – perhaps by changing them from complex to simple sentences.

Back at school
Display an OHT of the page with the verbs and subjects underlined in different colours. Children can mark their own, while the teacher helps with problems. From time to time ask them to find main verbs and subjects in texts.

p69 IT'S ALL RELATIVE

Objective
Revise work on complex sentences: ways of connecting clauses – relative pronouns. (Y6. T2, S3)

Lesson context
Teaching children to build longer, more interesting sentences.

Setting the homework
Some children may enjoy playing the game before working on the grammatical features of the solution. The game may be found online at: http://www.netcolony.com/arts/dungeons. A simplified text-based version of the game may be found in 100 Literacy Hours: Year 4 (page 130). A wide range of other text adventure games may be found at: http://www.helikon.com/Personal/Pete/Advents/arctitle.html.

Differentiation
All the children should be able to do the activity using their internalised knowledge of the language. The last sentence, however, presents a challenge.

Back at school
Go over the exercise with the class, but do not waste time trying to explain 'whom' – it is too difficult for the majority of children at this stage! Later, work with a small group of the most able to explore why this word is needed in this sentence.

p70 TALK, TALK

Objective
Revise appropriate use of punctuation: punctuating dialogue. (Y6, T2, S3)

Lesson context
A valuable preparation for writing a story with dialogue.

Setting the homework
Go over the explanation and example.

Differentiation
This exercise is aimed at children who have mastered the basics of punctuating dialogue and need to revise some of the more advanced features. The first two passages are easier because all punctuation, except speech marks, is provided. Children who have not mastered the basics should be given simpler tasks, eg placing speech marks before and after words spoken.

Back at school
Get the children to compare their work with a finished version on OHT. This frees the teacher to help with problems. The skill should be applied in context, ie by writing a story with dialogue.

p71 DASH IT!

Objective
Revise appropriate use of punctuation: dash and hyphen. (Y6, T2, S3)

Lesson context
Use as a follow-up to the reading of any text where dashes and/or hyphens are appropriately and effectively used.

Setting the homework
Go over the explanation at the top of the page.

Differentiation
This exercise should only be given to children who have a good grasp of more basic punctuation, as the concepts behind both are subtle and abstract. Less able children could be given a specific list of hyphenated spellings to learn.

Back at school
Emphasise to the children the importance of the dash and hyphen in their writing, in particular, the correct use of the hyphen in two-word numbers.

p72 FOLK HERO

Objective
Revise work on summary. (Y6, T2, S4)

Lesson context
Good preparation for writing about a story or novel, eg one way to start a literary essay is with a brief summary of the plot. Good preparation for writing blurbs, book reviews and introductions to books.

Setting the homework
Explain that the summary of a narrative is more difficult than the summary of a non-fiction text. Read each paragraph, then briefly retell the story in that paragraph in one's own words. The number of words can be counted and adjustments made .

Differentiation
Less able children could read the passage and write a few sentences describing each of Beowulf's three fights.

Back at school
A good summary will contain information about the four main sections of the narrative: the background information at the beginning, Beowulf's fight with Grendel, Beowulf's fight with Grendel's mother and Beowulf's fight with the dragon. There should be no additional description.

p73 ITALY

Objective
Revise work on note making (Y6, T2, S4)

Lesson context
This homework is a good preparation for note-taking.

Setting the homework
Explain that notes are personal reminders. They do not have to be written in sentences. The only criteria is that the user will be able to read and understand them. The second stage, writing a paragraph from the notes, should be done legibly.

Differentiation
Less able children could do the first task only, highlighting or underlining *any* ten facts. Other children should look for ten *key* facts. Most children should also undertake the second task.

Back at school
When marking, the main thing to look for is that the facts are taken from the whole passage and not from one or two paragraphs. The skill should be applied in a real context.

p74 BE AN EDITOR

Objective
Revise work on editing. (Y6, T2, S4)

Lesson context
This is good preparation for the final stage of an extended piece of writing as it provides a model which helps children to edit their own and each other's writing.

Setting the homework
Explain that there are two aspects to editing a text. One is proofreading, which is checking the text for mistakes in spelling, grammar and punctuation. The other, more creative aspect of editing, is making changes to improve the quality of the text.

Differentiation
Less able children should focus on the proofreading task. The more able could also do the extension activity.

Back at school
Use an OHP to display an edited text. This should contain, among other things, 15 corrected spellings, and deletions of the author's irrelevant personal opinions. The children should apply the same process to a piece of recent writing.

p75 IF

Objective
Use reading to investigate conditionals. (Y6, T2, S5)

Lesson context
Use as a follow-up to a text that contains conditionals.

Setting the homework
Conditionals have their complexities, not least of which is achieving the correct sequence of tenses. However, most native speakers of English, unless influenced by a strong regional or ethnic variety of English, will have internalised these rules. This activity focuses on two simple forms: 'If you can....you will' as in Kipling's poem and 'If + past tense...I would...'. All children need to know at this stage is that the word 'if' signals a conditional sentence.

Differentiation
Most children should use the 'If' poem template at the bottom of the page. However, more able children should be encouraged to develop the idea of an 'If' poem more flexibly.

Back at school
If time allows, read Kipling's poem and discuss what he is saying about what makes a man (by which we should understand a mature, wise adult). Ask children to read out their 'If' poems.

p76 SCHOOL RULES OK!

Objective
Investigate and use modal verbs. (Y6, T2, S5)

Lesson context
Use as a follow-up to any text where modals are used, or in the context of a study of verb tenses.

Setting the homework
Explain about *auxiliary* verbs. Auxiliary verbs are helper verbs which add to the meaning of main verbs. One kind of auxiliary verbs are *modals* which are used to express possibility, permission and obligation.

Differentiation
More able children might tackle the extension activity.

Back at school
Reinforce the concepts of possibility, permission and obligation as expressed by the modal verbs. Note that 'will' can often be used instead of 'must'. Ask the children who did the extension activity to read their additional rules, while other children listen to see if they can identify which modal verb has been used.

p77 A VICTORIAN VAMPIRE

Objective
Understand aspects of narrative structure – paragraph sequence. (Y6, T2, T1)

Lesson context
Exploring a text for paragraph and narrative structure, perhaps in preparation for writing a story.

Setting the homework
Explain the task, emphasising that every paragraph should be read before attempting to put them in order.

Differentiation
More able children should go on to the extension task.

Back at school
A correctly sequenced version of the text can be displayed on an OHT, while the children check their own work. Discuss the questions about linguistic signposts, eg 'Many years ago...' is a phrase which sets the scene for a story, 'Next day' is an indication of narrative sequence.

p78 ALIEN PARAGRAPHS

Objective
Analyse how individual paragraphs are structured in writing – fiction. (Y6, T2, T2)

Lesson context
This homework can be used as a preparation for story writing. It is equally effective when used at the redrafting stage, as it helps children to develop weak paragraphs.

Setting the homework
Remind the children of the basic rules: a new paragraph is marked by an indentation from the margin, not less than 1cm. Do not leave blank lines between paragraphs. Each paragraph should contain a number of sentences.

Differentiation
Less able children should apply the following rules: a new paragraph is shown by an indentation of approximately one centimetre. Each paragraph should contain two or more sentences. More able children should attempt the extension task.

Back at school
The skills should be applied in writing a story in paragraphs. The page could be consulted at the redrafting stage.

p79 VENETIAN PARAGRAPHS

Objective
Analyse how individual paragraphs are structured in writing – non-fiction. (Y6, T2, T2)

Lesson context
As a preparation for writing non-fiction or at the redrafting stage, as it helps to improve weak paragraphs.

Setting the homework
Remind the children of the basic rules for writing in paragraphs. Explain that in many non-fiction texts, new paragraphs are not indented and are marked by leaving a blank line. However, the example homework sheet uses indented paragraphs.

Differentiation
Less able children should practise applying the following rules: a new paragraph is shown by an indentation of approximately one centimetre. Each paragraph should contain two or more sentences. More able children should attempt the extension task.

Back at school
The skills should be applied in writing a non-fiction text in paragraphs. The page could be consulted at the redrafting stage.

p80 YOU!

Objective
Recognise how poets manipulate words – repetition. (Y6, T2, T3)

Lesson context
This homework could be set as part of a series of lessons on poetic techniques.

Setting the homework
Explain that, though the best-known poetic technique is rhyme, poets use many others. A very simple but effective technique is repetition. Emphasise that these poems work best when read aloud in pairs with a friend, parent or other adult.

Differentiation
All the children should be able to benefit from the tasks on the page.

Back at school
Ask the children to share their poems. They could perform them in pairs, while the rest of the class listen for repeated words or phrases.

p81 CARGOES

Objective
Recognise how poets manipulate words – connotations. (Y6, T2, T3)

Lesson context
This homework could be set as part of a series of lessons on poetic techniques or as preparation for the study of a poem which has particularly evocative diction.

Setting the homework
Explain *connotations*. Play a word association game. Part of the homework is to play this game using words in the poem.

Differentiation
Give less able children help with some of the more difficult words, in school, or a list of definitions could be sent home for the parent or helper.

Back at school
Discuss answers to the questions and the contrast presented in the poem between beauty and ugliness; between ancient and modern industrial civilisation.

p82 VERY LIKE A WHALE

Objective
Recognise how poets manipulate words – figurative language. (Y6, T2, T3)

Lesson context
As preparation for the study of simile and metaphor in poems.

Setting the homework
Revise the terms *simile* and *metaphor*: a simile is a comparison using 'like' or 'as'. A metaphor is a direct comparison. Read Lord Byron's poem *The Destruction of Sennacherib* to the children so they understand Nash's literary allusion in his poem.

Differentiation
There may be some children who are still struggling with the concept of simile (and metaphors are more difficult). These children should do some further work on similes, such as page 98, 'As blind as a bat'.

Back at school
Go over the metaphors and similes in the poem and ask what Ogden Nash thinks about them, that similes and metaphors are overused by poets. The children may suggest that the good point about similes and metaphors is that they help us to see the object in new and imaginative ways.

p83 SWIMMING SWAN

Objective
Investigate humorous verse. (Y6, T2, T4)

Lesson context
A good follow-up to the study of humorous poetry.

Setting the homework
This homework is more enjoyable and effective if read aloud in turns with a friend, parent or other adult.

Differentiation
All children should be able to read and enjoy these poems, though some will need the support of a helper. It is somewhat more difficult to say why they are funny, so children should be encouraged to use the clues given in the second question.

Back at school
Discuss what it is that makes each poem funny and share other humorous poems which any children have found or written.

p84 TWO BOYS CRYING

Objective
Analyse how messages, moods, feelings and attitudes are conveyed in poetry. (Y6, T2, T5)

Lesson context
The poem is a good preparation for a study of moods and feelings expressed in poetry and would lend itself to extended follow-up in a future literacy lesson (see below).

Setting the homework
Explain to the children that the poem they are going to read expresses strong feelings and has a powerful message. They should write their thoughts and feelings freely. Ask them to try to name the feelings. They may come up with words like 'greed' and 'selfishness' for the first boy, and 'despair' and 'hopelessness' for the second boy.

Differentiation
Less able children would benefit from reading the poem with a parent or other adult who could help them identify the feelings expressed in the poem. More able children could tackle the extension task.

Back at school
Share the children's reactions to the two boys. Ask the question: *The feeling of wanting something is just as strong in both boys. So what is the difference?* Discuss how the poet gets his message across: he does not preach at us; he just presents us with a contrast. If some children have written extra verses, select some to share with the rest of the class.

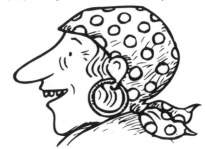

p85 INTRODUCING CLAIRE

Objective
Identify key features of different types of literary text: crime genre. (Y6, T2, T7)

Lesson context
Study of how to develop a character or study of the crime or detective fiction genre.

Setting the homework
Discuss the characters of detectives with whom the children are familiar from their reading and TV viewing. Explain that they are going to read about a detective who doesn't really conform to the character of the traditional detective!

Differentiation
Less able children should discuss the second part of the task.

Back at school
Discuss the character of Claire Voyant and how she and the conventional detective differ. Talk about the word play used for the character's name and the name of the 'author', Agnes Kirsty (a play on Agatha Christie's name).

p86 LA BELLE DAME SANS MERCI

Objective
Increase familiarity with significant poets of the past. (Y6, T2, T9)

Lesson context
As part of a series of lessons designed to increase familiarity with significant poets of the past.

Setting the homework
Give the children the following background information: John Keats was born in London in 1795. He studied medicine, but decided to be a poet. In 1820, he became ill with tuberculosis and died the following year. He is regarded as one of the finest poets of the nineteenth century. The title of the poem is in French because it refers to a medieval French legend. The title translates as: 'The beautiful lady without mercy'.

Differentiation
All children can read and enjoy the poem, particularly if it is shared. The summary could be oral rather than written.

Back at school
Encourage the children to read out the descriptions which they enjoyed and to explain why they liked them.

p87 FLASHBACK PLANNER

Objective
Write own story using flashbacks. (Y6, T2, T11)

Lesson context
Useful at the planning stage of a story. (For users of *100 Literacy Hours: Year 6*, the planner can complement that given in the Term 3 unit 'After ever happily'.)

Setting the homework
Children need time prior to the homework to think about ideas for a story, perhaps arising from stimulus material read in a lesson or outside of school. They could use the 'Crime cards' on page 88 of this book or the 'Victorian story cards' on pages 100–103 in *100 Literacy Hours: Year 6*.

Differentiation
Less able children should work with simpler plot types with a straightforward chronological sequence. More able children may manage a series of flashbacks. They should use the front of the planner for ideas, but develop complex plot outlines on the back.

Back at school
Ask the children to share their ideas for different types of plots with flashbacks. The next step is to begin work on turning the plans into fully developed stories.

p88 CRIME CARDS

Objective
Study in depth one genre and produce an extended piece of similar writing. (Y6, T2, T12)

Lesson context
As a stimulus for writing a story in the crime/detective genre.

Setting the homework
Give children the page of cards. Note that page 52, 'Character cards' can be used to broaden the scope of the resource. Explain that they should cut out the cards, shuffle them, then make up a story to fit the crime and alibi.

Differentiation
This game is accessible to all children, though some may need the concept of 'alibi' and some of the crimes explained.

Back at school
When playing the game, the children choose their cards at random. Tell them that they can now select their cards. They then build a new story around the cards, drawing on the experience of the homework.

p89 TELEVISION TROUBLES

Objective
Summarise different sides of an argument. (Y6. T2, T16)

Lesson context
This homework (along with pages 90, 92 and 93) belongs in a sequence of lessons on argument, which includes a great deal of oral work. When the children have had experience of expressing their arguments orally, they will find it easier to martial arguments in writing.

Setting the homework
Explain to the children that finding the main points is easier if they look for the paragraph divisions. Generally, there is a new main point in each paragraph.

Differentiation
Less able children should concentrate on the first task.

Back at school
When marking the summary, check that the children have included the five main points within the 50-word limit (give or take 10%) and that each summary reads as one coherent paragraph. The less able should have highlighted the five main points in each text. A valuable follow-up would be to have a class discussion or debate on the issue.

p90 DOLLY DEBATE

Objective
Identify personal opinion in an argument. (Y6, T2, T16)

Lesson context
This homework (along with pages 89, 92 and 93) belongs in a sequence of lessons on argument.

Setting the homework
Discuss the difference between fact and opinion and ensure that the children are clear about the difference.

Differentiation
Less able children should do the first task only.

Back at school
Discuss the passage, asking the children to point out the facts they found, then to point out the opinions. These could be marked in different colours on an OHT as the discussion progresses. The discussion can be extended to include views about whether the children agree or disagree with the article.

p91 THE DIRECTIONS GAME

Objective
Read and understand examples of instructions: directions. (Y6, T2, T17)

Lesson context
Use in the context of work on different types of instructions or work on the imperative mood.

Setting the homework
Emphasise that the most important thing about instructions is clarity. Directions are examples of instructions that everyone makes use of from time to time.

Differentiation
The more able should be encouraged to experiment with more and more complex directions.

Back at school
Share examples of directions. Discuss what it is that makes directions clear and what it is that makes them confusing.

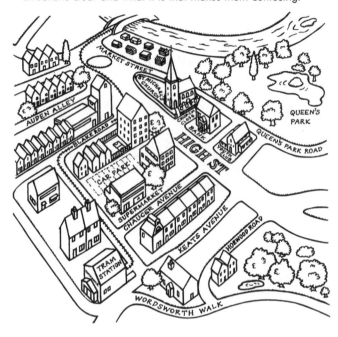

p92 HOW TO ARGUE

Objective
Construct effective arguments. (Y6, T2, T18)

Lesson context
This homework is most effective when used as an extension to page 93, 'Be controversial'. It is also very helpful in helping pupils to plan a debate speech.

Setting the homework
Provide stimulus material which is the basis for an argument. Ideas can be taken from newspaper articles, TV documentaries, essay titles. All children must go home with a clear idea of the subject about which they are going to construct an argument. Notes for this could be written on the back of the page.

Differentiation
This page is aimed at developing an argument in a fairly sophisticated way and is, therefore, not suitable for the less able whose argumentative skills are best developed through oral work. They could, therefore, be asked to prepare an argument with the help of a parent or another adult.

Back at school
The best thing to do with the arguments is to try them out on a real audience and see what counter-arguments are offered. Thus, a good follow-up would be to use the arguments in a debate.

p93 BE CONTROVERSIAL

Objective
Write a balanced report on a controversial issue. (Y6, T2, T19)

Lesson context
This homework (along with pages 89, 90 and 92) belongs in a sequence of lessons on argument.

Setting the homework
Children need to have experience of appropriate stimulus material, such as a debate, a discussion, or watching a documentary about a controversial issue. This will provide the raw material which the planner will help them to shape.

Differentiation
The planner is appropriate for most children as they are only asked to write two arguments for each side of the issue. More able children could extend this by writing several arguments for each side of an issue and ensuring that each argument is fully developed. Page 92, 'How to argue' will give them ideas for the different kinds of arguments. Notes for this could be written on the back of the page.

Back at school
The ideas on the planner should be translated into a piece of writing. This will be most effective if children are given a specific form and audience, eg write an article for a teenage magazine, write the script for a TV documentary for a general audience.

TERM 3

p94 SPELLING GUIDE

Objective
Revise and consolidate work from previous five terms.
(Y6, T3, W4)

Lesson context
A lesson or series of lessons focussing on tricky or difficult spelling or in preparation for any extended writing..

Setting the homework
Modifications can be made to reflect what has been taught. Ensure that the children understand they are writing a spelling guide for younger children. Each category needs a simple, clear explanation and some examples.

Differentiation
For less able children, delete the more difficult categories. More able children could prepare a booklet that covers more rules and examples.

Back at school
An ideal follow-up is to pair each child with a child from a younger year group and for them to help their partners with spelling, using the guide.

p95 NEW WORD GENERATOR

Objective
Invent words using known roots, prefixes and suffixes.
(Y6, T3, W5)

Lesson context
Following, or as part of a language investigation, such as Language Change or The History of English.

Setting the homework
Many new words draw on a common fund of prefixes, roots and suffixes, some of them very ancient. Many new words are based on whole existing words. They become the root of the new word. Explain to the children that the task involves using their imagination to invent some exciting and useful new words.

Differentiation
This activity is accessible to all, though the less able may need help with the meaning of some of the roots, prefixes and suffixes.

Back at school
Discuss the new words and what they mean. Create a piece of shared writing using these new words.

p96 WORD GAMES

Objective
Practise and extend vocabulary, eg through inventing word games. (Y6, T3, W6)

Lesson context
This homework can be set as an educationally valid form of light relief.

Setting the homework
Explain that the purpose of these games is both fun and educational. The children can play with a friend, parent or other adult. After playing each game, they should make up a similar one as instructed on the homework page.

Differentiation
Less able children should try out all the games, but only be asked to create one of their own of the kind they choose.

Back at school
The children could play each other's games. The children can return to the games at other times as they are fun, relaxing, yet can improve the children's vocabulary and spelling.

p97 A HANDSOME BEAST

Objective
Practise and extend vocabulary, eg through inventing word games such as riddles. (Y6, T3, W6)

Lesson context
This homework goes well with a study of rhyming poetry. The riddles are written in rhyming couplets, so the children will get more experience of the pattern of rhythm and rhyme, but in a fun way.

Setting the homework
It is a good idea to do the first riddle in class, so the children know what to do when they get home.

Differentiation
All the children can have a go at these riddles with the help of a friend or adult.

Back at school
Go over the answers. These are: deer, bat, bear, rat, adder, horse, hare, panda, zebra.

p98 AS BLIND AS A BAT

Objective
Experiment with language by creating similes. (Y6, T3, W7)

Lesson context
Shared or guided poetry reading or writing, where the focus is on the use of simile.

Setting the homework
Revise the definition of a simile: a comparison using 'like' or 'as', eg 'as blind as a bat', 'the moon was like a silver ball'. The homework gives a list of well-known similes and the task is to think of a new, original version of each one. Read the first simile which has been done as an example.

Differentiation
This homework should represent a consolidation of concepts which the children have been developing over a couple of years. It should, therefore, be suitable for all children. Differentiation will be by outcome.

Back at school
Ask children to share their new versions of the *similes*.

p99 YOUR EYES ARE LIKE

Objective
Experiment with language by creating similes. (Y6, T3, W7)

Lesson context
Writing poetry and, in particular, developing imaginative expression.

Setting the homework
Revise the definition of *simile* (see notes for previous page). Briefly, explain the homework page by taking the children through the instructions to show how the sample poems were inspired. Advise them that they will need a dice.

Differentiation
It may be sufficient for some children just to practise writing the format of the basic 'like' *simile*, using their two rolls of the dice, eg 'Your eyes are like a box of chocolates.'

Back at school
Ask the children to share their *simile* poems. The next step is to apply the same flexibility of imagination to longer and more developed poems.

p100 WEREGIRL

Objective
Revise the language conventions and grammatical features of narrative texts. (Y6, T3, S1)

Lesson context
As preparation for, or during, the study of a particular narrative text. It can also be used as a preparation for writing this kind of text.

Setting the homework
Explain to the children that they should read the short text sample, then write notes in the blank boxes, eg the note in the first box might read: 'The subject of the story is a girl who turns into a werewolf. This would belong to the horror genre'. The second part of the task is to write similar notes about another narrative.

Differentiation
Less able children should do the first task only. Provide a story as the basis for the second task for those who need it.

Back at school
Use discussion of the homework as a lead-in to a class or group study of a specific narrative.

p101 HENGEST

Objective
Revise the language conventions and grammatical features of recount texts. (Y6, T3, S1)

Lesson context
As preparation for, or during, the study of a recount text. It can be used as a preparation for writing this kind of text.

Setting the homework
Explain to the children that they should read the text sample, then write notes in the blank boxes, eg the note in the first box might read: 'The subject of the story is an historical account of Hengest'. The second part of the task is to write similar notes about another recount.

Differentiation
Less able children should do the first task only. Provide a recount for the second task for those who need it.

Back at school
Use discussion of the homework as a lead-in to a class or group study of a specific recount.

p102 ASTEROID BLASTER

Objective
Revise the language conventions and grammatical features of instructions texts. (Y6, T3, S1)

Lesson context
As preparation for, or during, the study of a particular instructions text. It can also be used as a preparation for writing this kind of text.

Setting the homework
Explain to the children that they should read the text sample, then write notes in the blank boxes, eg the note in the first box might read: 'The subject of the instructions is how to install and play a computer game'.

Differentiation
Less able children should do the first task only. Provide an instructions text for the second task for those who need it.

Back at school
Use discussion of the homework as a lead-in to a class or group study of a specific instructions text.

p103 IN THE ATLANTIC

Objective
Revise the language conventions and grammatical features of report texts. (Y6, T3, S1)

Lesson context
As preparation for, or during, the study of a particular report text. It can also be used as a preparation for writing this kind of text.

Setting the homework
Explain that of all text types, reports are the most varied. They can be anything from a school report with a few sentences for each subject, or a parliamentary report running to several volumes. The example is a report on a scientific experiment. The children should read the report, then write notes in the boxes, eg the note in the first box might read: 'The subject of the report is an experiment about falling temperature in air and water'.

Differentiation
Less able children should do the first task only. Provide a report text for the second task for those who need it.

Back at school
Use discussion of the homework as a lead-in to a class or group study of a specific report text.

p104 THE STEAM ENGINE

Objective
Revise the language conventions and grammatical features of explanation texts. (Y6, T3, S1)

Lesson context
As preparation for, or during, the study of a particular explanation text. It can also be used as a preparation for writing this kind of text.

Setting the homework
Explain that they should read the text, then write notes in the boxes, eg the first box might read: 'The subject of the explanation is how a steam engine works'.

Differentiation
Less able children should do the first task only. Provide an explanation text for the second task for those who need it.

Back at school
Use discussion of the homework as a lead-in to a class or group study of a specific explanation text.

p105 CAPITAL PUNISHMENT

Objective
Revise the language conventions and grammatical features of persuasive and discursive texts. (Y6, T3, S1)

Lesson context
As preparation for, or during, the study of a particular persuasive or discursive text. It can also be used as a preparation for writing this kind of text. It could be linked with homework page 92, 'How to argue' and page 93, 'Be controversial'.

Setting the homework
Explain that both persuasive and discursive texts argue a point of view. Persuasive texts argue for one side of an issue, whereas discursive texts examine both sides.

Differentiation
Less able children should do the first task only. Provide a persuasive or discursive text for the second task for those who need it.

Back at school
Use discussion of the homework as a lead-in to a class or group study of a specific persuasive or discursive text.

p106 ME AND MY GIRL

Objective
Conduct detailed language investigations: rhyming slang. (Y6, T3, S2)

Lesson context
Preparing for a language investigation, possibly as part of a module on Language Variety.

Setting the homework
Explain the concept of language variety (or dialect). Speakers from different regions and ethnic groups speak with variations to the grammar and pronunciation of standard English.

Differentiation
All children should be able to read and enjoy this text and carry out the tasks with the help of an adult.

Back at school
Follow up with an investigation appropriate to your locale. Some children may wish to explore their ethnic variety of English. All they need are some suitable texts as a starting point. For areas without noticeable dialects, some general topics are: Find out more about Rhyming Slang, Compare British and American English.

p107 MINI-ZAPPER

Objective
Revise formal styles of writing. (Y6, T3, S3)

Lesson context
Preparing for, or during, the study of formal writing.

Setting the homework
Explain that formal and informal styles are not a question of right and wrong, but a question of fitness for purpose.

Differentiation
Less able children should appreciate the difference in tone between the two letters; they will need help finding the differences.

Back at school
Discuss the differences that the children found between the formal letter and the informal note, eg:
Language: Compare 'undertaking this operation yourself' with 'If you do it yourself'.
Style: The formal letter uses the passive voice 'The Engineering Department may be contacted…'
Greetings and closures: 'Dear Mr' and 'Yours sincerely' are the correct formal way to open and close a letter. Compare with the friendly and informal 'Hi Bob' and 'Cheers'.
Contractions: The informal note contains lots of contractions.

p108 MAKE IT MORE COMPLEX!

Objective
Secure control of complex sentences, understanding how clauses can be manipulated to achieve different effects. (Y6, T3, S4)

Lesson context
Following a series of lessons in which each method of combining clauses has been studied.

Setting the homework
Recap on the main points of your class lessons. Explain to the children that, even when they are not sure about the terminology, they should still try to write a sentence in each box.

Differentiation
If this is too advanced for some, let them work on simpler ways of combining clauses, eg page 44, 'Using conjunctions'.

Back at school
Discuss the examples. Encourage the children to apply these methods in their creative writing.

p109 HANSEL AND GRETEL

Objective
Secure control of complex sentences, understanding how clauses can be manipulated to achieve different effects. (Y6, T3, S4)

Lesson context
This activity provides practice in applying the skills developed on complex sentences.

Setting the homework
Recap on the different ways of building sentences and combining simple sentences to make complex ones. Discuss the example on the sheet.

Differentiation
Most children will be able to expand this text using their innate knowledge of the structures of the English language.

Back at school
Ask selected children to read their expanded texts and look at the different techniques used. This will help all children to make their implicit knowledge explicit.

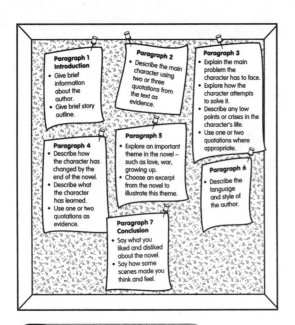

Paragraph 1 Introduction
• Give brief information about the author.
• Give brief story outline.

Paragraph 2
• Describe the main character using two or three quotations from the text as evidence.

Paragraph 3
• Explain the main problem the character has to face.
• Explore how the character attempts to solve it.
• Describe any low points or crises in the character's life.
• Use one or two quotations where appropriate.

Paragraph 4
• Describe how the character has changed by the end of the novel.
• Describe what the character has learned.
• Use one or two quotations as evidence.

Paragraph 5
• Explore an important theme in the novel – such as love, war, growing up.
• Choose an excerpt from the novel to illustrate this theme.

Paragraph 6
• Describe the language and style of the author.

Paragraph 7 Conclusion
• Say what you liked and disliked about the novel.
• Say how some scenes made you think and feel.

p110 NOVEL TEMPLATE

Objective
Describe and evaluate a novel. (Y6, T3, T1 slightly adapted)

Lesson context
This homework should be set towards the end of the study of a novel.

Setting the homework
A range of work needs to have preceded this homework, eg chapter summaries, character studies, creative responses (such as letters to characters). This template is designed to support writing about the novel as a whole. Explain to the children how they can adapt their previous work to provide material for this essay. For example, an earlier character study could be summarised for paragraph 2.

Differentiation
The less able could use the simpler template, on page 120, 'Book-o-meter'.

Back at school
Share the final paragraphs – the personal response section of the essay.

p111 LOST AND FOUND

Objective
Discuss how linked poems relate to one another. (Y6, T3, T2)

Lesson context
This homework can be used to explore the two linked poems, or in a study of William Blake, perhaps along with his work on pages 113 and 114 and his poems in *100 Literacy Hours: Year 6* (pages 158–9).

Setting the homework
If this homework is set in the context of a study of William Blake, it would be instructive to look at the links Blake made in the rest of his work, eg between other pairs of poems, and between books of poems, ie *Songs of Innocence* and *Songs of Experience*.

Differentiation
Most children should be able to read and enjoy these poems thanks to Blake's deceptive simplicity. Encourage the less able to read the poems and discuss their answers to the questions with a parent or other helper.

Back at school
Find other poems which would link with these thematically, ie poems on childhood, lost children. Try browsing through poetry anthologies to find other poems which are linked in some way.

p112 POET-O-METER

Objective
Describe and evaluate the style of an individual poet. (Y6, T3, T3)

Lesson context
This homework should follow the study of several poems by a single poet.

Setting the homework
Discuss the question: *What makes a good poet?* This will help the children to fill in their poet-o-meter more judiciously. Criteria could include: interesting subject, vivid descriptions, good use of simile and metaphor, skill with rhythm and rhyme. Give the children a new poem by the poet to use with this activity.

Differentiation
This fun activity is accessible to all, though the more able could be encouraged to write a more extensive report by continuing on the other side of the page.

Back at school
Discuss the responses and work out an average score for the poet (based on the 'recommendation ratings'). This could be done throughout the year so that an ongoing 'top ten' of poets could be displayed on the class notice board.

p113 THE SCHOOLBOY

Objective
Comment critically on the overall impact of a poem. (Y6, T3, T4)

Lesson context
This homework could be set in the context of a study of William Blake, or of poems on the theme of children or school.

Setting the homework
If possible, enlarge the homework sheets to A3 size to provide more space for writing. Explain that the sheet is designed to encourage a comment for each verse.

Differentiation
Children who have not yet grasped the concept of figures of speech should omit questions on that subject. More able children could respond to the questions on a separate sheet of paper which will allow them to answer each one more fully.

Back at school
Discuss the comments that the children made for each verse.

p114 MEMORABLE FANCIES

Objective
Compare and contrast the work of a single writer. (Y6, T3, T5)

Lesson context
This homework could be set in the context of an extended study of William Blake, or it could be used as a follow-up to a homework or class lesson on a Blake poem.

Setting the homework
Explain that most writers write in many different styles and about different subjects, but their work also has things in common. The homework page contains one of Blake's *Memorable Fancies*, which are not poetry, but imaginative prose.

Differentiation
The language and content of *Memorable Fancies* is difficult, so this homework is not suitable for less able children. They could instead, compare and contrast two of Blake's simpler poems. See, for example, page 111, 'Lost and found'.

Back at school
Ask the children to share and discuss what they have written in the table at the bottom of the page.

p115 DAPHNE AND BRITNEY

Objective
Look at connections and contrasts in the work of different writers: poem/song. (Y6, T3, T6)

Lesson context
This homework could be part of a study of a selection of poetry on the theme of love, or the development of English.

Setting the homework
Explain that the homework consists of comparing two poems on the theme of love. One was written in the 16th century and the other is a pop-song lyric written a few years ago.

Differentiation
All children can read and enjoy the poems, but finding the connections and contrasts is more difficult. Less able children should talk about these with a parent or helper.

Back at school
Discuss the connections and contrasts between the two poems. For example: subject matter: both are written to girls who do not return the writer's love; form: both are written in rhyme, though the pattern of rhyme is different; figures of speech: both writers compare the girl's blonde hair to gold, but the other figures of speech are different; time: words like 'a-piece', 'do hold', 'inthrones', show that the poem was written a long time ago, whereas words like 'disco' and 'boogie-woogie' show that the song was written recently; setting: perhaps the poem was set in a garden, whereas the song is certainly set in a disco.

p116 GRIMM'S BEAM

Objective
Look at connections and contrasts in the work of different writers: fairy tales. (Y6, T3, T6)

Lesson context
Set in the context of a study of a number of other fairy tales.

Setting the homework
Make notes on the features of a contrasting fairy story, using the same categories – a good choice would be one with a similar theme but from another culture.

Differentiation
Less able children can read and enjoy the story and should also be able to comment on characters and settings.

Back at school
Discuss the connections and contrasts between 'Grimm's Beam' and the other fairy story studied.

p117 NIGHT CLOUDS

Objective
Annotate a passage in detail in response to specific questions: a poem. (Y6, T3, T7)

Lesson context
This is an appropriate homework when studying figurative language in any poem or group of poems.

Setting the homework
The specific question is 'make notes on the figurative language in the poem'. It is, therefore, important that the children understand the term, *figurative language*. Revise this using the 'Dear Helper' note on the bottom of the page.

Differentiation
Children who are struggling with any of the above should be given a homework on the easiest figure of speech: the simile. See page 98, 'As blind as a bat'.

Back at school
Discuss the notes which the children made.

p118 HOUSECARLE

Objective
Write summaries of books or parts of books. (Y6, T3, T9)

Lesson context
Shared reading and study of a novel, biography or other long text. This homework is a good preparation for writing chapter summaries and should be set before the first chapter summary is required. Note that, in a sequence of work, a summary could be required for each chapter, but for the sake of variety and to avoid boredom, it is better to ask for summaries of key chapters or ask each child to summarise a different chapter.

Setting the homework
Read the passage then write about it from memory. Check that specifics like names of people, places and dates are correct.

Differentiation
Less able children could read the passage with a helper and give an oral summary.

Back at school
Apply the technique to the book which is being studied.

p119 BOOK JACKET

Objective
Write a brief synopsis of a text, eg for back cover blurb. (Y6, T3, T10)

Lesson context
This is one of a range of creative response activities which can be used in the study of a novel, biography or other book.

Setting the homework
Decide for which book each child is going to design a jacket. Ideal candidates are old hardbacks, books with out-of-date covers, extracts from books in anthologies or textbooks and children's own stories. Emphasise that they must think up some new design ideas! Display a real book jacket and show how the diagram on the sheet relates to the real thing.

Differentiation
All children should be able to do this activity to some degree. You may omit certain features for some children.

Back at school
Translate the design ideas into reality. Get each child to make the physical book jacket by cutting thick paper to size and making folds to fit the book. The main areas should be ruled using light pencil, then the final drawing and lettering can begin.

p120 BOOK-O-METER

Objective
Write a brief review tailored for a real audience: children of their own age. (Y6, T3, T11)

Lesson context
Shared or guided reading of a novel, biography or other book.

Setting the homework
A book must have been read.

Differentiation
This page is suitable for use with children of all abilities. If desired, the more able could be asked to use page 110, 'Novel template', which will provide them with support for writing a literary essay about the book they have read. Note, however, that the latter is most appropriate at the end of a detailed study of a book, whereas the book review is most appropriate as a follow-up to reading for enjoyment.

Back at school
Book reviews could be posted on a notice board so that the children can read each other's reviews and, perhaps, be inspired to read some of the reviewed books.

p121 SKYLARK

Objective
Compare texts, drawing out their different styles and preoccupations. (Y6, T3, T12)

Lesson context
This is a good follow-up to a lesson which focuses on the question, 'What is poetry?' By comparing a poem with a prose text, it is possible to highlight its unique features.

Setting the homework
Revise the terms *prose* and *poetry*. Prose is ordinary writing, set out in sentences and paragraphs. Poetry is imaginative writing, often using rhythm and rhyme. Discuss the different purposes of prose (entertainment, information, instructions) and poetry (imaginative expression).

Differentiation
If these texts are too difficult for some children, prepare a resource page with a simpler prose passage and poem.

Back at school
Discuss responses to the questions.

p122/p123 FAIRY TALE CARDS 1 & 2

Objective
Write an extended story: fairy tale. (Y6, T3, T14)

Lesson context
This set of cards is designed to be used as a stimulus for story telling. The cards are best used after a study of some examples of the fairy tale/fantasy genre. (If using *100 Literacy Hours: Year 6*, they are an ideal follow up to a study of Propp's Functions).

Setting the homework
Demonstrate how to use the cards.

Differentiation
All the children can succeed at the oral stage of story telling. Indeed, experience has shown that children who are held back by poor literacy skills, can often excel in other areas such as oral story telling. Only children of average ability and above should be asked to write down the story unaided.

Back at school
Ask for volunteers to tell their oral stories to the class. The next stage is to build on this experience of oral story-telling. Tell the children that they can now choose their cards and that they are going to make up a story which includes all the best features of the different examples they have made up or heard orally.

p124 SPIDERS

Objective
Retrieve information quickly from a text by skimming and scanning. (Y6, T3, T17/18)

Lesson context
Use as a preparation for a research task (probably in another area of the curriculum) which will involve children in skimming and scanning a range of texts for information.

Setting the homework
Demonstrate the difference between skimming and scanning. 'Skimming' is skipping over the text quickly, looking for key words and phrases. When a key word or phrase has been found, the eye 'scans' along the lines of text to see if it is relevant. If so, that section of text is read normally and the required information is noted.

Differentiation
Differentiation can be provided by adjusting the time limit.

Back at school
Apply the skill in a research context.

p125 COR!

Objective
Divide whole texts into paragraphs: fiction. (Y6, T3, T21)

Lesson context
This is a good preparation for writing a story in paragraphs, or revising paragraphing skills before redrafting. Note that this text provides a good complement to page 78, 'Alien paragraphs'.

Setting the homework
Revise reasons for starting a new paragraph, eg step forward in time, flashback, change of scene, change of viewpoint, new character. Emphasise that these are not rigid rules.

Differentiation
Less able children should divide the text into five paragraphs.

Back at school
When marking the work, accept any sensible division into paragraphs. However, it is a mistake if there are too many paragraphs, eg almost every sentence, and a mistake if there are too few, ie there should be at least three. Children should apply the skill to writing or redrafting a story.

p126 EUTHANASIA

Objective
Divide whole texts into paragraphs: non-fiction. (Y6, T3, T21)

Lesson context
This is a good preparation for writing a persuasive or argumentative essay in paragraphs, or revising paragraphing skills before redrafting.

Setting the homework
Revise the reasons for starting a new paragraph, eg a new argument, counter argument, introduction or a conclusion. Emphasise that these are not rigid rules but just guidelines.

Differentiation
Less able children could be asked to find the introduction and conclusion and mark as separate paragraphs, then to find at least two paragraphs in between.

Back at school
When marking the work, accept any sensible division into paragraphs. However, it is a mistake if there are too many paragraphs, eg almost every sentence, and a mistake if there are too few. Introduction and conclusion should be in separate paragraphs and there should be at least two others in between. Children should then apply the skill to writing or redrafting an argumentative or persuasive essay.

p127 FORM FINDER

Objective
Select the appropriate style and form to suit a specific purpose and audience. (Y6, T3, T22)

Lesson context
Teaching writing for specific purpose with a specific audience.

Setting the homework
Explain the importance of fitness for purpose in writing. Writers have to be clear about what their purpose is, who their audience is, and what is the most suitable form for the subject about which they want to write. The children will need a couple of dice.

Differentiation
Children should generate a series of choices about which to write, eg writing a musical about cloning to impress an expert would be a harder than writing a letter about a holiday to entertain your best friend!

Back at school
Children could have fun reading out the results of their random combinations and the written work arising from them.

Spelling quiz

- Ask a helper to give you this spelling quiz.

1	government	6	know
2	island	7	accept
3	Wednesday	8	too
4	daughter	9	quiet
5	February	10	their

11	libraries	16	couldn't	21	believe
12	railways	17	won't	22	receive
13	shelves	18	I'm	23	chief
14	diagnoses	19	she's	24	ceiling
15	women	20	they're	25	inconceivable

26	accelerating	31	flexible	36	business
27	bathing	32	existence	37	enough
28	bubbling	33	magnificent	38	guess
29	calculating	34	boundary	39	queue
30	celebrating	35	acceleration	40	separate

- Check your spellings against the list above. For each group of five words, write your score in the box below. If you scored three or less, look in the box below to see which type of word you need to revise.

1–5	6–10	11–15	16–20	21–25	26–30	31–35	36–40
silent letters	homophones	plurals	contractions	ie / ei	e / ing	confusing endings	often mis-spelt

---

Dear Helper,

Objective: to identify own needs for spelling revision.

Read the word to your child clearly, but with normal pronunciation. Make up a short sentence to make the meaning of the word clear. Say the word again and give your child time to write it down. When your child has completed the quiz, help them to check their score.

Letter sequences

You can improve your spelling by looking for patterns in words. These patterns include **letter sequences**. A **letter sequence** is a common pattern of letters which can occur at the beginning, end, or in the middle of a word.

Example: rhy - this letter sequence can help you to remember two related words: **rhy**me and **rhy**thm.

- Find words which include these letter strings. Use a dictionary to help you.

cou-	dia-	gui-	mea-

-ession	-rous	-ough	-scien-

Remember to make use of the two spelling tips when learning new spellings!

Spelling Tip 1
Improve your spelling by looking for patterns in words.

Spelling Tip 2
When learning a new spelling, find more words which share a letter sequence and learn those at the same time.

Dear Helper,

Objective: to use known spellings to help spell words with similar patterns.

Encourage your child to look for letter sequences in words and to learn several words with the same letter sequence at the same time.

Confused?

Root of word				Ending
adapt	comfort	collaps	fashion	**able**
ador	change	desir	imposs	**ible**
aquaint	appear	circumfer	coincid	**ence**
confid	brilli	arrog	defi	**ance**
assist	adolesc	inhabit	consist	**ent**
reluct	compet	hesit	irrelev	**ant**
annivers	burgl	compuls	diction	**ary**
bound	compliment	contradict	introduct	**ory**
adventur	boister	chor	carnivor	**ous**
ambiti	camp	cauti	nucle	**us**
solu	exten	ambi	investiga	**sion**
dimen	addi	confu	decora	**tion**

● Cut out the **Root of word** cards and the **Ending** cards for each section. Then, try the different endings with each root. When you think you have the right combination, write the word down and check it in a dictionary.

Spelling Tip
When learning how to spell words with several syllables, say them to yourself as they are written, not as they are said – for example, instead of 'adaptUHBLE', say 'adaptABLE'.

Dear Helper,

Objective: to learn to spell words with confusing endings.

Practise saying words with several syllables out loud with your child, saying them as they are spelt rather than as they are pronounced: eg relevANT, not relevUHNT.

Name: _____

Building on roots

- See how many words you can make from each word box, for example:
  con struct ion, de struct ively. Write them in the **'Your words'** column.
  Check the meaning of any word you are unsure of in the dictionary.

Prefix	Root	Suffix	Your words
con	struct (build)	ion	
de		ive	
inde		ively	
in		ure	
ob		able	
re		or	
bio	graph (write)	er	
geo		s	
para		y	
photo		ical	
radio		ing	
tele		ic	
contra	dict (say)	ionary	
pre		ory	
ver		ator	
-		ate	
-		ion	
-		s	

Extension

- Find prefixes and suffixes to go with the following Greek and Latin roots: bio (life), spec (look/see), log (word/science), phon (sound), tech (skill), volv (roll).

Dear Helper,

Objective: to use prefixes, roots and suffixes to help with spelling.

An awareness of roots, prefixes and suffixes can help with spelling and vocabulary. If necessary, remind your child of the following definitions: a root is the basic part of a word to which other parts can be added to change the meaning – a prefix at the beginning and a suffix at the end.

Connect it

- Learn the spellings and meanings of the list of **connectives** shown below.
- Ask somebody to test you on the spellings (or use **look, cover, write, check**).

consequently	indicates that something happens as a result of what has just been written.
eventually	after a time.
for example	(sometimes abbreviated e.g.) used to introduce an example.
for instance	this means the same as the above, but cannot be abbreviated.
further	(or furthermore) used to add another point of the same kind.
however	used to introduce a different point which qualifies or limits the previous point.
in addition	used to add another point.
in any case	used to say that, even though there are some problems, the point that follows is still true.
in brief	used to sum up a previously expressed idea briefly.
in other words	used to introduce a simplified version of a previous statement or to state the conclusion of an argument.
meanwhile	used to explain something that is happening at the same time as something else.
moreover	used to add another point.
nevertheless	used to state the main point, after an opposing point has been discussed.
notwithstanding	similar to 'nevertheless'.
on the contrary	used to introduce an opposite point of view.
on the other hand	similar to 'on the contrary'.
on the whole	used to sum up a paragraph or an argument.
otherwise	used to say that if something is not done, the following will happen for that reason (similar to 'consequently').
therefore	used as a summary point.
whereas	used to compare points.

Dear Helper,

Objective: to learn the meanings and spellings of connecting words.

Connecting words will improve both the flow and meaning of your child's writing. When testing your child's spelling, read the word clearly, but with normal pronunciation.

Can you speak Anglo-Saxon?

- Say out aloud these words for parts of the head. Then, sort and write the words in two columns: **Similar to modern English** and **Different to modern English**.

heafod

feax

eare

eage

nosthril

nosu

weleras

sweora

Similar to modern English	Different to modern English

- Can you guess what these words are in modern English?

tungon	
fystum	
handa	
fot	
earm	

Dear Helper,

Objective: to understand how words have changed over time.

Have fun with this activity. Join in with your child, attempting the pronunciations. Try having a conversation using the words!

Name:

Sir Bedivere

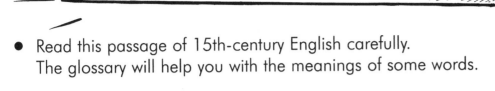

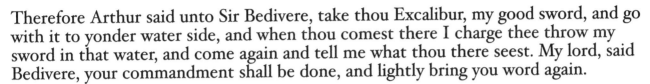

- Read this passage of 15th-century English carefully.
  The glossary will help you with the meanings of some words.

Therefore Arthur said unto Sir Bedivere, take thou Excalibur, my good sword, and go with it to yonder water side, and when thou comest there I charge thee throw my sword in that water, and come again and tell me what thou there seest. My lord, said Bedivere, your commandment shall be done, and lightly bring you word again.

So Sir Bedivere departed, and by the way he beheld that noble sword, that the pommel and the haft was all of precious stones; and then he said to himself: If I throw this rich sword in the water, thereof shall never come good, but harm and loss. And then Sir Bedivere hid Excalibur under a tree. And so, as soon as he might, he came again unto the king, and said he had been at the water, and had thrown the sword in the water. What saw thou there? said the king. Sir, he said, I saw nothing but waves and winds. That is untruly said of thee, said the king, therefore go thither lightly again, and do my commandment; as thou art dear to me, spare not, but throw it in.

Caxton's edition of Malory's, Le Morte D'Arthur, Volume 2, 1485 (modernised spelling)

Glossary of archaic words in order of appearance in text			
thou	you	beheld	looked at
yonder	over there	pommel, haft	handle of sword
comest	come	thereof	of it
charge	order	thee	you
seest	see	thither	there
commandment	order	art	are
lightly	gladly		

- Now, rewrite the passage, translating it into good modern English which would be simple enough for someone of your age to understand easily. The first line has been done as an example.

Modern translation:
Arthur said to Sir Bedivere: 'You must take my sword, Excalibur, over there to the river bank...'

Dear Helper,

Objective: to understand how words have changed over time.
The lack of speech marks makes the original passage more difficult to read. Try reading it as a dialogue with your child.

PHOTOCOPIABLE

Place names

- Look at the place name elements in the left-hand column and use a map of Britain to find other examples for the right-hand column.

Origins of place name	Your examples
From the Celts aber – mouth of a river, eg Aberystwyth coombe – deep valley, eg Ilfracombe glen – narrow valley, eg Glenrothes pen/ben – a hill, eg Ben More **From the Romans** chester/caster – fort, eg Winchester, Doncaster coln – town, eg Lincoln port – gate or harbour, eg Portsmouth strat – or – street – road, eg Stratford **From the Anglo-Saxons** dun – hill, eg Maldon ford – ford, eg Wickford ham – hamlet, eg Rotherham ing – people of, eg Barling ley – clearing, eg Keighley mere – pond/lake, eg Windermere tun – village/town, eg Edington worth – enclosure, eg Kenilworth **From the Scandinavians** toft – house, eg Langtoft by – farmstead, eg Denaby thorpe – isolated farm, eg Goldthorpe thwaite – meadow, eg Braithwaite	

Extension

- Look at a map of your area. Using coloured pens for the four influences, eg Celts, write down as many place name elements as you can find. Which appears to be the main influence on place names? Work out the meaning of the place names and what you might find there.

Dear Helper,

Objective: to research the origins of place names.

You can work with your child on this activity, sharing the research. A road atlas is ideal for reference.

Personal names

- Read the list of names, their origins and their meanings.
- Add your own favourites to the list and try to find out their meanings.

Names and their origins	Meaning
The Bible David Michael Eve Sarah	friend Who is like God? life princess
Saints Christopher George Catherine Barbara	bearer of Christ farmer – St George slew a dragon pure – St Catherine was tortured foreign
Latin and Greek Calvin Cecil Julia Melissa	bald blind descended from Jove (Roman god) honeybee
India Krishna Shiva Sita Anand	dark – name of Hindu god beginning – god of destruction furrow – goddess of harvest happiness
Your favourite names	**Meaning**

- Choose names for these characters.

Dear Helper,

Objective: to research the origin of personal names.

Talk with your child about why his or her name was chosen. Discuss the names of other family members or friends.

New words

- Read the list of new words and say why you think each was needed (the first one has been done as an example).
- Make up your own new words. Good sources are: anything to do with computers, new inventions, modern slang.

New word	Meaning	Why we need it
chairperson	someone who presides over a meeting	The word does not imply gender discrimination, as does 'chairman'.
audiophile	a person who loves sound (made from a Latin and a Greek root)	
carjacking	hijacking a car – a combination of *car* and *hijacking*	
e-mail	a shortened form of *electronic mail*	
fantabulous	a combination of *fantastic* and *fabulous*	
ginormous	a combination of *gigantic* and *enormous*	
internet	a worldwide network of computers	
modem	a device to allow a computer to use a phone line	
mouse	an old word with a new meaning – a device to operate a computer	
pooper-scooper	a device to pick up pet droppings	
road rage	extreme anger caused by traffic	
snail mail	postal service (slow compared to e-mail)	
tagging	a form of graffiti	
vertically-challenged	a politically-correct way to describe a short person	
Y2K	the year 2000	

Extension

- There are many different ways to make up new words. How many can you find in the list?

Dear Helper,

Objective: to understand how new words are made up.

Words are continually being added to our vocabulary in order to talk about new inventions and ideas. Words also drop out of use. Try thinking of some of these with your child – eg 'abide', 'behold', 'verily'.

Where in the world?

anorak ☐	shampoo ☐
yacht ☐	cola ☐
café ☐	astronaut ☐
bungalow ☐	typhoon ☐
alphabet ☐	kangaroo ☐
piano ☐	maize ☐
guerilla ☐	banana ☐
loch ☐	tattoo ☐
judo ☐	tomato ☐

- Follow these instructions to investigate word origins (etymology).
  - In your dictionary, find the code used to show from which language words come – eg F = French; Sp = Spanish; Du = Dutch.
  - Enter the code in the box.
  - Cut out each word and paste it on your world map.

Extension

- Browse through the dictionary to find other words that originate outside the United Kingdom and add them to your map.

Dear Helper,

Objective: to use a dictionary to discover the origin of words.

Some words may come from more than one language. The child may wish to copy them several times and place them on the map appropriately.

Parts of speech circus

- Read the poem, then add more examples in the box beside each couplet.
- Try to learn the poem to help you remember simple definitions for the parts of speech.

Parts of speech circus	More examples
A **Noun** is a word that is a name, Like *Big Top, ring, performer, game.*	
An **Adjective** describes a noun, Like *joyful* juggler, *clever* clown.	
A **Pronoun** can a noun replace: *Her* acrobatics, *his* funny face.	
A **Verb** describes things being done: *Performing, joking, having fun.*	
An **Adverb** helps by telling how: *Skillfully, funnily, later, now.*	
Conjunctions join two words together: Lions *and* tigers, wind *or* weather.	
Prepositions show how words relate, As *in* the circus, *on* a plate.	
An **Interjection** shows surprise: *Ah* how clever! *Oh* how he flies!	
Connectives link ideas together, As *on the other hand, however.*	
The **Articles** which you will meet, A and *the,* make our list complete.	

Extension

- Try to write a new version of the poem by changing the examples in the second line of the first seven couplets.

Dear Helper,

Objective: to revise parts of speech.

It is not vital that your child knows all the parts of speech. This activity is part of the learning process. Encourage your child to recite the poem to you to aid learning it by heart.

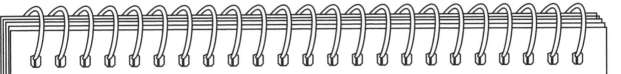
The Great Eastern

Notes on the Great Eastern

scrapped in 1889

five funnels of 30 metres high and six masts which could carry sails

designed by Isambard Kingdom Brunel – famous Victorian engineer

launched in 1858

designed to carry passengers from Britain to Australia without having to stop for coal on the way

failed to make a profit and was converted for cable laying

stress is said to have led to death of designer

took five years to build

remembered as ship that laid first Atlantic cable

211 metres long

two paddle wheels and one propeller

longest ship in world until Oceana launched in 1899

37 metres wide

many delays in building ship

What to do

- Cut out the notes and put them in order, grouping notes about similar topics together.
- Make the notes into sentences, many of which could begin with 'The Great Eastern.......', 'The ship.......', or 'She.......'.
- Combine some of the short sentences into longer ones.
- Experiment by re-expressing the sentences in a different order. When you are satisfied, write out your final version.

Dear Helper,

Objective: to use notes to make sentences.

Remind the child that a sentence is a unit of language which makes sense on its own. Sentences begin with a capital letter and end with a punctuation mark such as a full stop or a question or exclamation mark.

PHOTOCOPIABLE

Barbara Allan

• Adapt this ballad into a story for children or a longer, more detailed story for adults. An example is given at the bottom of the page.

It was about the Autumn time,
When thick the leaves were falling,
That Sir John Graeme of the West Countrie
Sent word for Barbara Allan.

His men went out to Scarlet Town
To the place where she was dwelling,
Saying: "Haste and come to my master,
If you are Barbara Allan."

"There's sorrow printed on his face
And death is o'er him stealing,
And he is sick, and very sick,
For love of Barbara Allan."

She said, "If sorrow's on his face
And death is o'er him stealing
Then little better shall he be
For a sight of Barbara Allan."

But then at last she went with them
And came where he was lying.
She drew his bed curtain, and said:
"Young man, is't true you're dying?"

"O, I am sick, and very sick
And it's all for Barbara Allan!"
"I'll never help you now, " she said,
"Though your heart's blood were spilling."

"Don't you remember when," said she,
"As another maiden's gallant,
You danced the hall around, around
And slighted Barbara Allan?"

He turned his face unto the wall
Since she of hope bereft him.
"Farewell," she said as she got up
And to his sorrow left him.

She had not gone a mile or two
When she heard church bells knelling
And every peal the death bell gave
Cried: "Woe to Barbara Allan!"

"O, mother, mother, make my bed,
O, make it soft and narrow.
Since my love died for me today,
I'll die for him tomorrow."

Example: A story version

As Sir John looked out of his bedroom window, he saw the Autumn leaves falling. He felt very sad since he had fallen out with Barbara Allan. He decided to send his servants out to look for her and ask her to come to see him. In the meantime, he felt so ill, that he got back into bed.

His men went to Scarlet Town where Barbara Allan lived...

Dear Helper,

Objective: to adapt a text for a different purpose and reader.
Encourage your child to read the whole ballad through first, then to take a verse at a time and tell you in modern English what it is saying.

In the future

- Look at the table which shows three forms of the future tense.

Future tense	Using 'will' + base verb	Using 'will be' + present participle	Using 'going to' + base verb
Example	She *will post* the letter.	I *will be running* my own business.	I am *going to travel* to the moon for a holiday.

- In the box below, write your predictions for the future in two paragraphs.

What the world will be like when I am 25

What I think I'll be doing when I am 25

- Choose three different coloured pencils or highlighter pens, one for each future tense you have used. Mark each example with the correct colour code.

Dear Helper,

Objective: to revise the future verb tense.

Remind your child that the tense of a verb tells us when something happened. The present tense is used for something happening now, the past tense for something that already happened and the future tense for something that will happen in the future.

Active and passive

In an **active** sentence, the active person or thing comes before the verb (in the example below, the active thing is the police). In a **passive** sentence, the active person or thing comes after the verb.

> **Active:** The police found Trevor this morning.
> **Passive:** Trevor was found by police this morning.

Active and **passive** sentences emphasise different things. In the example above, the active sentence emphasises the police and the passive sentence emphasises Trevor. When writing, choose active or passive to get the emphasis you want.

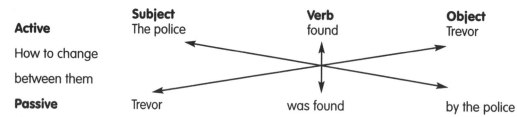

Changing from **active to passive**

	Subject	Verb	Object
Active	The police	found	Trevor
How to change between them			
Passive	Trevor	was found	by the police

• Make these **active** sentences **passive.**

The chicken crossed the road.
Samantha found the treasure chest.
The surgeon saved the child's life.
Shakespeare wrote *Hamlet*.
The snow covered the ground.

• Make these **passive** sentences **active.**

The naughty boy was punished by the teacher.
The Haywain was painted by John Constable.
The television was invented by John Logie Baird.
The *Titanic* was sunk by an iceberg.
The princess was saved by the dragon.

Extension

• Explain the differences in emphasis between the original sentence and the changed sentence.

Dear Helper,

Objective: to understand the difference in emphasis between active and passive sentences.

Another way of explaining the difference between active and passive which may help your child is that active sentences are where someone or something 'does' and passive sentences are where someone or something 'is done to'.

Using connectives

Connectives are words and phrases used to connect ideas.
Connecting words and phrases do different jobs.

- Make sure you know how to spell the **connective** words below.
- Think of more examples and add them to the appropriate box.
- Complete the passage below by adding appropriate **connectives**. Take care to spell them correctly.

Addition	Opposition	Cause	Time
To add things	To show a different point of view	To show that something causes something else.	To indicate the times when things happen
and	but	because	then
also	however	so	after
furthermore	although	therefore	finally
in addition	nevertheless	this means	meanwhile
besides	on the other hand	consequently	subsequently

Ghosts

Lots of people claim to have seen ghosts _____ there is no scientific evidence that ghosts exist.

_____ I have never seen a ghost myself even though I have been in many 'spooky' places. Once I spent

a night in Burton Agnes Hall (which is supposed to be haunted by a screaming skull) _____ I wanted a

first-hand experience. _____ I didn't hear or see a thing. _____, I have been in lots of old churches

when it was dark and seen nothing.

To make me believe in ghosts, I would need to see two kinds of evidence. _____, I would want to see a

video or a photograph (_____ not a fake). _____, I would have to have the evidence of my own eyes.

_____, I don't think this can ever happen _____ I will carry on not believing in ghosts!

Dear Helper,

Objective: to investigate connecting words and phrases.
The passage shows that connecting words and phrases can appear at the start of a sentence as well as in the middle. Point out to your child how this helps to vary the writing.

PHOTOCOPIABLE

Using conjunctions

Conjunction Cards

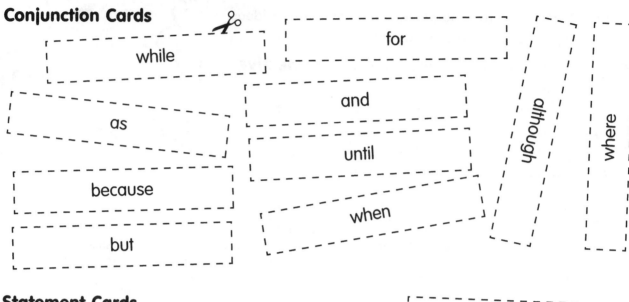

while

for

as

and

until

because

when

although

where

but

Statement Cards

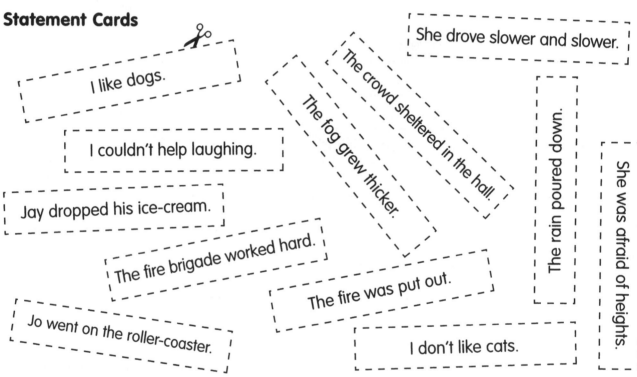

I like dogs.

She drove slower and slower.

I couldn't help laughing.

The crowd sheltered in the hall.

The fog grew thicker.

Jay dropped his ice-cream.

The rain poured down.

She was afraid of heights.

The fire brigade worked hard.

The fire was put out.

Jo went on the roller-coaster.

I don't like cats.

- Cut out the conjunction and statement cards and experiment with different ways of making complex sentences out of each pair of statements.
- Experiment with using conjunctions at the beginning of the sentence as well as in the middle and write down the best examples.

Extension

- Write 6 sentences which contain two statements linked by conjunctions.

Dear Helper,

Objective: to investigate connecting words and phrases.

Conjunction is the term used to describe a word or phrase that connects sentences, phrases or other words. Your child should understand that the choice of conjunction can affect meaning.

Name:

Make it complex

- The examples below show some of the ways of forming complex sentences by using different connecting devices. Write your own examples in the empty boxes.

Use a **conjunction** between two statements to join them together.

Example:	She raided the refrigerator because she was hungry.
Your example:	

Use a **conjunction** at the beginning of a sentence to join two statements together. Note the comma between the statements.

Example:	Although it was cold, he went out without a coat.
Your example:	

If appropriate, combine the information in statements into a **list** (separate each item except the last with a comma).

Example:	My friend hates maths, PE, English and most other subjects.
Your example:	

Insert a **phrase in apposition** (a phrase of extra information) into a sentence between two commas.

Example:	The doctor, though an elderly man, was very up to date.
Your example:	

Begin a sentence with a **participle** (the -ing form of a verb) to join two statements together. Note that a comma is used to mark off the first phrase.

Example:	Climbing the stairs to the attic, I slipped and twisted my ankle.
Your example:	

Dear Helper,

Objective: to use connecting words or phrases to form complex sentences.
Encourage your child to experiment with different ways of connecting points or ideas and to evaluate which links work best.

Note what follows

Use a **colon** to mean 'note what follows'. Its commonest use is to introduce a long list, or a list of bullet points.

The **semi-colon** can be thought of as a stronger comma. One of its uses is between groups of items in a long list.

Example:
In the torture chamber I saw the following items: a sharp, blood-stained axe; some ropes, chains, and manacles; and an iron-maiden which was a sort of box full of nails.

- Punctuate this long list. Use a **colon** to introduce the list and two **semi-colons** to separate the main items. Then, go back and see if any commas are needed.

In the mutant section of Hollywood Horror Park I saw lots of terrible creatures a vamwolf which is half vampire half werewolf a mumeton which is half mummy half skeleton and a zombiegeist which is half zombie and half poltergeist

- Write a list like the example at the top of the page which includes groups of objects in this picture.

List of objects:

Dear Helper,

Objective: to learn how to use the colon and semi-colon.
The colon and semi-colon are sophisticated punctuation marks. Sometimes, it is difficult to know which to use and sometimes, either is appropriate. So, encourage your child to experiment and, when they've made a decision, to explain their choice.

Pop it in

Sentences are often extended by putting in extra information. This is called **parenthetical** information. The extra information can be inserted and marked off in three ways.

Using **commas:**   With only one small ship, *The Pelican,* Drake sailed into the Pacific.

Using **dashes:**   He struck the match – his last – with trembling hands.

Using **brackets:**   *Kidnapped* was written by Robert Louis Stevenson (who also wrote *Treasure Island*).

Using **commas** is the normal way of inserting extra information.
Dashes give a much stronger effect – making the extra information stand out.
Brackets show that extra information is useful, but optional and can be ignored if desired.

- Experiment with combining these sentences and extra information using different types of punctuation. Choose which type of punctuation you think is best.

Sentences	Extra information
Timothy was ill-suited to police work.	a pale, nervous young man
Gutenberg lived in the German town of Mainz.	who invented the printing press
William Shakespeare was voted the best writer of the last millennium.	1564–1616
The ship was powered by two steam turbines.	a turbine is a rotary engine
Tom's friend was reported missing after the battle.	the best friend he'd ever had

Dear Helper,

Objective: to learn how to use commas, dashes and brackets to put extra bits of information into sentences.

By investigating how extra information is added to sentences, children will be able to experiment in their own writing. Look for other examples with your child in newspapers, magazines and books.

The film of the book

- Read a book from which a film has been made. When you have read the book, fill in the left-hand column.
- When you have watched the film, fill in the right-hand column and the evaluation box.

Book title:

Author:

Date (of first publication):

Plot: Write a brief summary of the story.

Character: Describe the main character. How did you imagine him/her?

Action: Describe an exciting scene.

Film title:

Director:

Date (of first release):

Plot: Describe any changes to the story.

Character: How was this character portrayed in the film?

Action: Describe how this scene was filmed and any special effects.

Evaluation: Do you think the film is a good adaptation of the book?

Dear Helper,

Objective: to compare a book and a film.

This activity gives your child the opportunity to compare two popular media forms. If you've also read the book and/or seen the film, share your ideas and discuss the similarities and differences in treatment.

Name:

Viewpoint

- Read the story beginnings and answer these questions about each story:
  - Who is the main character in each story (where names are not given, write a phrase of description, eg the captain of a spaceship)?
  - Who is telling each story (eg the author, a character in the story)?
  - Which person (1st, 2nd or 3rd) is each story written in?

Story 1

I wish I had never been sent here. It's always cold and wet – not like my own country. The countryside is bleak and empty, and the nearest town is miles away. Wait a minute – who's this coming?

'Halt! Stop and be searched!' The man doesn't seem to understand, so I bar his way. He stops and then I search his pack. He's just another poor peddlar. I let him through the gate. The rain starts again – where's my cloak? Yes, the life of a Roman soldier on Hadrian's wall is very hard...

Story 2

CHOC DROPS

Timothy was always causing trouble. He used to fall out with his little sister, never eat his tea, never do his homework and never go to bed on time. Everybody who had to put up with him agreed that he was a real nuisance.

One day, Timothy was gulping down a tube of chocolate drops instead of eating the lovely dinner of mashed potatoes, toad-in-the-hole and Brussels sprouts that his mother had made for him, when his dad called him into the lounge...

Story 4

Captain's Log, 28th September 2020

We have arrived at our destination in a safe orbit around Jupiter. However, I am concerned about a minor computer malfunction. The computer says we are orbiting Saturn – and, come to think of it, the planet does have rings. I wonder if I've got miles and kilometres mixed up again...

Story 3

You are standing in a medieval church. The church is empty and it is getting dark. A dull booming noise is coming from the direction of the church tower. There are three exits: door to the tower, door to the crypt, door to the outside – and safety. Which way will you go?

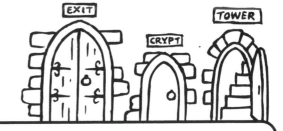

Dear Helper,

Objective: to understand viewpoint in a story.

If your child needs support, remind them that 'I' or 'we' usually indicates that the story is autobiographical or that one of the characters is telling the story in the first person. 'He' or 'she' usually indicates that the author is telling the story from an outsider's perspective in the third person. 'You' indicates a second-person narrative where the reader is the one being written about.

PHOTOCOPIABLE

Little Blue Denim Jacket

- Read this modern retelling of a well-known fairy story and underline or highlight the modernised parts.
- Either: try out the idea yourself using a different story as a starting point. Or: write a different ending to this version, starting after '...*she took a short cut through the woods*'.

There was once a girl who loved wearing blue denim so much that people called her Little Blue Denim Jacket. One day she was having fun surfing the net, when her mother asked her to take a pizza to her grandmother.

'Have I got to go?' moaned Little Blue Denim Jacket.

'Yes, you must go and thank her for that lovely present she sent you.'

'What, you mean that horrible red riding hood?'

'Yes – and I think you should wear it to show your appreciation!'

'I'm not wearing that hideous thing – it makes me look like something out of a fairy story!'

'I think it's very pretty!'

Little Blue Denim Jacket sighed, 'Why couldn't she have given me a mobile phone instead? Then I could have phoned her to say thank you.'

'You won't get any more presents if you don't do as you're told!' snapped her mother.

So Little Blue Denim Jacket put on the little red riding hood and set off for her grandmother's. But as soon as she was out of sight of the house, she pulled the little red riding hood off and threw it into a ditch. Then she did something else she was not supposed to do – she took a short cut through the woods. She had not gone far, when she saw a wolf. She badly wanted to run away, but she kept very still, hoping that, like the T-Rex in 'Jurassic Park', its vision depended on movement. It didn't: the wolf came right up to her, sniffed her, and to her immense surprise, spoke.

'I'm looking for a girl wearing a little red riding hood,' said the wolf. 'Seen her?'

Little Blue Denim Jacket pointed to the place where she had thrown down the little red riding hood, and the wolf, much to her relief, went away.

When she arrived at Grandma's house, she found Grandma in floods of tears.

'It's all my fault!' she sobbed.

'What is?' asked Little Blue Denim Jacket.

'This!' sobbed Grandma, showing her the headlines in the morning paper: GIRL IN LITTLE RED RIDING HOOD EATEN BY WOLF!

'But Grandma!' exclaimed Little Blue Denim Jacket. 'It's me and I'm safe. I – er – dropped my little red riding hood, and the wolf must have found it and torn it up!'

'Bless me! So it is and so you are. What a relief!' said Grandma giving Little Blue Denim Jacket a great big hug.

'You know, the world is such a dangerous place these days that I think I'll buy you a new present that will keep you safe!'

'What will it be this time?' said Little Blue Denim Jacket a little doubtfully.

'A mobile phone, of course!' said Grandma.

Little Blue Denim Jacket was so pleased that she visited her grandma every day, safe in the knowledge that that she could always call for help on her mobile phone. And they all lived happily ever after.

Dear Helper,

Objective: to write a modern retelling of a well-known story.

Encourage your child to read the story aloud. Then, discuss another favourite traditional tale that could be modernised – or think of alternative endings to this story. Choose one you both like and write it up.

100 LITERACY HOMEWORK ACTIVITIES • YEAR 6 TERM 1

Name:

Story planner

- Use the notes in these three columns and the boxes at the bottom of the page to plan a story in three sections: **Beginning, Middle** and **End.**

- Write your plan on the back of this sheet (or on another sheet) under the headings: **Beginning, Middle** and **End.**

	Problem	**Quest**	**Flashback**
Beginning	• Begin by writing a paragraph about the person who has the problem.	• In the first paragraph, describe a character and the reason for their quest (a quest is a search for something).	• The first paragraph should be an action-packed scene from the 'middle' of the story.
Middle	• Write a paragraph about what happens when the problem starts. • Write a paragraph about what happens when the problem is at its worst: this is the 'climax' of the story. • Write a paragraph explaining the main character's plans to solve the problem.	• The middle of the story is a series of adventures which the character has along the way.	• The story now goes back to the real beginning so that the reader knows what is on going on and how the exciting scene came about. • The flashback ends and, in the next few paragraphs, the action continues from the first scene.
End	• In the final paragraph, explain how the problem is solved and the main character is happy.	• The last paragraph should describe how the character completes the quest and gets the reward.	• In the last paragraph, the main character remembers the exciting scene that began the story.

Other types of ending

Proverb	**Twist in the tale**	**Anti-climax**	**Circular**
• This kind of story is planned to end with a moral or a proverb which sums up what happens in the whole story.	• Something happens at the end which makes us look back on it in a different way, eg one of the people we thought was good, turns out to be the villain.	• The middle should build up to a climax, but the end should show that it was not exciting after all, eg a person thinks he saw a ghost, but it turns out to be a trick of the light.	• This ending should bring the reader right back to the beginning, eg a poor boy who gets rich, and then loses all his money.

Dear Helper,

Objective: to plan the plot and structure of a story.

This is a resource sheet that your child will use on many occasions when planning their story writing. Encourage your child to talk through their story ideas, giving your comments, before writing notes under Beginning, Middle and End.

Name:

Character cards

- Think of a name for each of these characters and write it in the box.
- Choose two contrasting characters and write a detailed character sketch for each.

Dear Helper,

Objective: to plan the characters in a story.

Having an idea of how characters might behave and talk, as well as how they look, is an important part of story writing. Support your child by asking questions – for example: *What colour is the character's hair? Is the character kind or cruel? Do they talk in posh or colloquial language?*

100 LITERACY HOMEWORK ACTIVITIES • YEAR 6 TERM 1

Solar summary

- Read this description of the solar system and summarise it in one paragraph of approximately 150 words. Follow these steps:
  - Highlight the topic sentence in each paragraph.
  - Count the highlighted words.
  - Highlight extra information until you have approximately 150 words.
  - Copy out what you have highlighted in one paragraph.
  - Change the wording, where necessary, so that it reads well and makes sense.

The Solar System

The solar system is the group of planets that revolve around the sun. There are nine planets, many of which have moons. Our own planet, Earth, is the third planet.

The planets travel around the sun in approximately circular orbits. Mercury's orbit is nearest the sun. Next is Venus, then Earth, Mars, Jupiter, Saturn, Uranus, Neptune, and finally Pluto. Pluto's orbit is the most elliptical of any of the planets.

The four inner planets are made up of rock and iron. However, the four largest outer planets, Jupiter to Neptune, are gas giants. These planets are composed mostly of hydrogen and helium in gaseous form. Pluto is much smaller than the other planets and is composed mainly of nitrogen.

Seven of the planets have moons. Saturn, with 24, has the greatest number. Earth and Pluto both have one moon. Jupiter's Ganymede and Saturn's Titan are larger than the planet Mercury.

Until recently it was thought that only one planet, Saturn, had rings. However, space probes have shown that Jupiter, Uranus and Neptune also have rings. These rings are made up of millions of small rocks.

The question of life on other planets has fascinated scientists since they began to study the night sky. About a hundred years ago, it was thought that Venus was covered with a dense rain forest which might contain life. However, recent probes have shown that its atmosphere is made up of carbon dioxide and sulphuric acid and that its surface temperature is too high for life forms to survive.

Mars is now one of the most likely places to contain life. Though the Mariner space probes (1969) proved that there are no 'canals' on Mars, they did show that surface water once existed, so there is the possibility that simple life forms might have lived there. Future Mars probes are planned which will investigate this question more fully.

Dear Helper,

Objective: to summarise a passage in a given number of words.

Summarising is an important skill for children to learn, particularly when researching information in reference material. The 150-word target is an approximate number of words. A range of 135 to 165 is quite acceptable.

From story to script

- Turn this extract from a story into a playscript, as in the example below.

One day, Timothy was gulping down a tube of chocolate drops instead of eating the lovely dinner of mashed potatoes, toad-in-the-hole and Brussels sprouts that his mother had made for him. Suddenly, his dad called him into the living room. He was sitting in the middle of the room with the video recorder in pieces all around him.

'Here, hold this,' said Dad. He gave Timothy a small red object with two tiny wires sticking out.
'What is it?' said Timothy.
'It's the sensor for the remote control. Don't lose it!'
Suddenly Mum shouted from the kitchen.
'Timothy! Come and get your dinner this minute – or else!'
Timothy jumped, gulped down his last handful of sweets – and choked as something stuck in his throat! He coughed and spluttered. Then Mum, who had come to fetch him, patted him on the back, and the obstruction went down.
'Oh no!' groaned Dad.
'What is it?' said Mum.
'Timothy's just swallowed the sensor for the remote control!'
Mum panicked.
'Quick! Fetch a doctor!'
'I'm all right, Mum,' said Timothy. 'It wasn't much bigger than my sweets.'
'It'll pass through him in a couple of days,' said Dad. 'Trouble is, I've got to buy a new sensor now.'
By dinner time next day, the video recorder had been repaired and Dad was testing it out. He put a video in the slot and pressed 'play'. The video began to play. Timothy stopped falling out with his little sister and began to play quietly by himself. Dad pressed 'stop'. The video stopped. Timothy stopped.
'Hey! It works!' shouted Dad. He pressed 'search' just to make sure. The video searched quickly through the programme. Timothy searched quickly through his school bag. Timothy's sister couldn't believe her eyes.

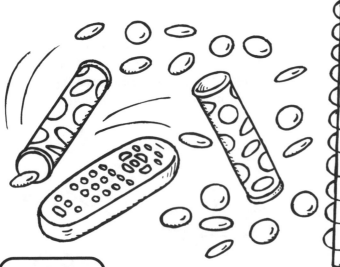

Example playscript

Scene 1: The living room. We can hear Timothy arguing with his sister off stage. Dad is kneeling in front of the video recorder with a screwdriver in his hand muttering to himself.

DAD:	(shouting loudly) Timothy! Come here!
TIM:	Coming.
DAD:	Here, hold this.

(Gives him a small red object with two tiny wires sticking out.)

Dear Helper,

Objective: to write a short section of a story as a playscript.

The example should help your child with the conventions of setting out a playscript. Read the story out loud with your child, each taking different character parts, so that how a line should be spoken is identified and can be incorporated as directions in the script.

100 LITERACY HOMEWORK ACTIVITIES • YEAR 6 TERM 1

Personification poems

Personification is describing things as though they had human qualities.

- Read **'Storm'**, and underline the human qualities in the description.

Storm
Don't be so angry,
Stop howling around my house,
Banging windows wildly,
Breaking branches bad temperedly,
Pushing my dustbin over on purpose.
I'm stressed out as well,
But I don't scream and shout about it.

- Write your own personification poems under the headings below.

Winter

Fear

Extension

- Now choose a title of your own and write a personification poem.

Dear Helper,

Objective: to write poems that use personification.

Encourage your child, when reading poetry, to look out for examples of personification.

Evaluating reports

- Use the headings in this chart to evaluate a report.
- Make notes in each box.
- Write a paragraph in the Summary box which brings your notes together.
- Give a star rating (5 is high).

Subject Explain briefly the subject of the report.	
Language Is the language clear to the ordinary user or is it too technical? Give some examples.	
Data What kind of data is used in the report? How is it presented? Is it easy to understand?	
Accuracy Is there any evidence of the accuracy of the information provided in the report?	
Conclusions Does the report give a clear summary of conclusions and perhaps recommendations for action?	
Summary	
Star rating	

Dear Helper,

Objective: to evaluate a report.
Children should be encouraged to comment critically on the language, style and accuracy of reports as this is a practical skill that will be important in later life.

Name:

Evaluating instructions

- Use the headings in this chart to evaluate an instruction manual.
- Make notes in each box, or over the page.
- Write a paragraph in the Summary box.
- Give a star rating (5 is high).

Layout Is it clear or cluttered? Does it use: numbers? bullets? symbols?	
Language Is the language clear to the ordinary user or is it too technical? Give some examples.	
Diagrams Are diagrams used? If so, are they clear and easy to understand? Are they clearly labelled?	
Navigation Can you find your way to information easily (eg by using contents, index, subheadings)?	
Trouble–shooting Is there a trouble-shooting guide, contact telephone numbers or email addresses?	
Summary	
Star rating	

Dear Helper,

Objective: to evaluate instructions.

Try to find examples of different types of instructions and share these with your child – eg recipes, appliance instructions, car manuals. Are they clear and easy to understand? If not, what would help to make them better?

Biography frame

● Use this frame to write a biography.

Name of person:

Paragraph 1: why they are remembered
(for example: _____ is remembered for ......)

Paragraph 2: early life, education and rise to fame
(for example: _____ was born in_____ on [date].....)

Paragraph 3: an obstacle overcome or a problem solved
(for example: _____ was faced with a big challenge which was ....)

Paragraph 4: achievement 1
(for example: _____'s first major achievement was......)

Paragraph 5: achievement 2
(for example: Another major achievement was.....)

Paragraph 6: end of life and summary of achievements
(for example: _____ died in [date] after......)

Dear Helper,

Objective: to develop the skills of writing a biography.
Talk with your child about the person for whom they are writing the biography. For example, ask: _Why did your child choose this person to write about? Are there qualities about the person you admire or dislike?_

Journalists' jargonator

- Read the words and phrases below. Find out the meanings of words you are not sure about.

Jargon words

blaze	louts	fact-finding	penetrating	walkabout
breakthrough	scroungers	grass-roots	saga	watchdog
crisis	shock	kiss-and-tell	inflationary	whitewash
cut	probe	low-key	soaring	plummetting
drama	in-depth	meaningful	swingeing	
euro-	charter	ministerial	tongue-lashing	
media	copycat	ongoing	unemployment	

Jargon phrases

and that's official	is balanced on a knife edge	is getting off the ground
shock horror	is bending over backwards	hands are tied
since records began	laid off	is keeping a finger on the pulse
is alive and well	politically-correct	very real
is like a hole in the head	of many years standing	spin doctor

- Now, read this example of how to write an exciting article.

Before:

Litter in the playground

Our headteacher, Mrs Mellow, told pupils in assembly that she was worried that litter in the school playground was getting worse. She said that it was a serious problem and that pupils who drop litter will be punished.

After:

Litter Crisis

Headteacher Mrs Mellow is bending over backwards to solve the school's litter crisis. Her recent in-depth, fact-finding survey showed that the school's litter problem was the worst since records began. 'This is a very real problem,' she said as she gave the entire school a tongue-lashing in assembly. 'We need litter in the playground like a hole in the head! Litter louts will be punished and that's official!' More news on the school's litter drama in our next edition.

- Write your article about school, home or local news using the jargonator.

Dear Helper,

Objective: to develop a journalistic style.

Explore the words and phrases with your child, explaining any unknown words. Look for examples of these words in newspapers you have at home. Discuss how the *before* and *after* versions of the example differ. Ask: *Why is the 'after' version a better read?*

Suffixes plus

Rules for adding suffixes

Rule 1:   Drop the final **e** before a suffix beginning with a vowel.
            Example: sense + ible = sensible

Exceptions: Keep the final **e** before a suffix beginning with **a** or **o** if it is
            necessary to retain the soft sound of the **c** or **g**.
            Example: advantage + ous = advantageous

Rule 2:   Keep the final **e** before a suffix beginning with a consonant.
            Example: care + ful = careful

● Complete the table below, taking care to follow the rules.

Word	+ Suffix	= New word
achieve	ment	achievement
advance	ing	
approve	al	
compare	able	
continue	ous	
courage	ous	
defence	less	
desire	able	
guide	ance	
hope	ful	
nine	ty	
pronounce	able	
retire	ing	
scare	ing	
separate	ing	
severe	ly	
taste	less	
true	ly	
use	ful	
whole	ly	

Dear Helper,

Objective: to revise spelling rules for adding suffixes.

If necessary, remind your child that a suffix is a letter or group of letters added to the end of a word to change its meaning: eg walk/walk**ed**; book/book**s**; slow/slow**ly**; fashion/fashion**able**.

Number prefixes

● Add examples to each section, using a dictionary to help.

Prefix: uni-	Meaning: one
unicorn	a mythical horse with **one** horn

Prefix: mono-	Meaning: one
monotone	sound with **one** tone

Prefix: bi-	Meaning: two
bicycle	a cycle with **two** wheels

Prefix: tri-	Meaning: three
triangle	a figure with **three** sides

Prefix: quad-	Meaning: four
quadrangle	an open space with four sides

Prefix: multi-	Meaning: many
multi-storey	a car park with many storeys

Extension

● Find words with these number prefixes: sex-, sept-, oct-, non-, cent-, mil-.

Dear Helper,

Objective: to revise spelling rules for adding prefixes that indicate number.

If necessary, remind your child that a prefix is a letter or group of letters added to the beginning of a word to change its meaning. Watch out for bi- and tri- words. For example, 'bitter' has nothing to do with 'two' and 'trick' has nothing to do with 'three'.

From curro to courier

- Study the list of Latin roots, then try to match them with the modern English words below. One has been done as an example.

Latin roots		Meaning	English word
aqua	-	water	courier
audio	-	hear	final
curro	-	run	fort
finis	-	end	liberty
fortis	-	strong	pendant
liber	-	free	malady
malus	-	bad	navy
manus	-	hand	plain
navis	-	ship	aquatic
pendeo	-	hang	regal
planus	-	level	manual
plus	-	more	scripture
poto	-	drink	prospect
porto	-	carry	rotate
pro	-	before	audience
rego	-	rule	visible
rota	-	wheel	eruption
ruptus	-	broken	potion
scribo	-	write	surplus
video	-	see	porter

Extension

- Find more modern English words made from these roots.

Dear Helper,

Objective: to learn more about the origin of words.

See if your child knows the meaning of the modern English words given. If not, help them use a dictionary to find out.

All that glisters

- Read the proverbs and write an explanation in the second bubble (the first has been done as an example).
- Collect more proverbs (ask your family) and write them on the back of the sheet.

1

All that glisters is not gold.

Just because something looks valuable does not mean to say it is.

2

All work and no play makes Jack a dull boy.

3

Don't count your chickens before they hatch.

4

When the cat's away, the mice will play.

5

A stitch in time saves nine.

6

People in glass houses shouldn't throw stones.

7

Familiarity breeds contempt.

Dear Helper,

Objective: to collect and explain proverbs.

A proverb is a wise, traditional saying, often used to teach a lesson. Help your child add to the collection with sayings you have heard over the years.

Past times

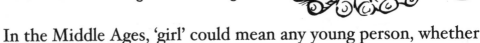

- Read the word histories below.
- Write a short article for the *'Past Times'* using some of these words with their original meanings.

GIRL: In the Middle Ages, 'girl' could mean any young person, whether male or female.

GUY: The Gunpowder Plot of 1605 was celebrated by the burning of the effigy of Guy Fawkes. This effigy was known as a 'guy'. Later, the word 'guy' meant anyone shabbily dressed. In America, the term describes any person, male or female.

NAUGHTY: In the Middle Ages, 'naughty' meant 'having naught', in other words, poor. It came to mean 'inferior', then 'wicked'. However, this term refers now to the misbehaviour of children.

NICE: In the Middle Ages, it meant 'foolish'. Later, it came to mean 'fastidious' and then later still anything pleasant or good. Today, it is overused as a vague, descriptive adjective.

SILLY: In the Middle Ages, it meant 'blessed', but gradually it lost its status. Now it means 'foolish'.

VILLAIN: The medieval word, 'villein' meant a poor, uneducated farm labourer. Perhaps because they sometimes turned to crime, the word came to mean 'criminal'.

Past Times

(continue on the back of the sheet)

Extension

- Try to find out some more word histories.

Dear Helper,

Objective: to understand that the meaning of words can change over time.

Share with your child any words you know whose meanings have changed since you were a child.

Argument words

However on closer inspection...

- Read the list of **words** and **phrases** used in argument.
  Look up the meaning of any words of which you are not sure.

Words

allows	generates	mirrors	represents
creates	indicates	problems	reveals
discloses	influences	produces	shows
exemplifies	initiates	provokes	suggests
expresses	inspires	reflects	symbolises

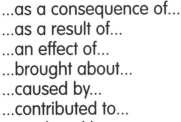

It is often argued that.......

Phrases

...an outcome of...
...as a consequence of...
...as a result of...
...an effect of...
...brought about...
...caused by...
...contributed to...
...produced by...
...shows evidence of...
...stemmed from...

However, on closer inspection...
In discussing whether or not...
It is often argued that...
My conclusion is that...
My point of view is...
On one side of the issue...
On the other side of the issue...
There are both advantages and disadvantages in...
Therefore, after examining all the arguments...
After examining both sides of the argument...

- Now add your own examples. Find examples in newspaper articles and books.

Words	Phrases

Dear Helper,

Objective: to build a bank of words and phrases used for argumentative or persuasive writing.

Arguments, especially written arguments, use a wide range of words and phrases to compare and contrast ideas. Help your child to look through newspapers, magazines and books to find other examples of argument words and phrases.

Active inventors

- Complete the table by filling in the blanks. The first one has been done for you. Then think of examples and write them in both **active** and **passive** voices for the last four rows.

From active	To passive
In these **active** sentences, the focus is on the person or thing that 'does'.	In these **passive** sentences, the focus is on the person or thing 'done to'.
Brunel designed the Great Western Railway.	The Great Western Railway was designed by Brunel.
Vivaldi composed *The Four Seasons*.	
Fritz Lang directed the film, *Metropolis*.	
	The music for *Jurassic Park* was written by John Williams.
	The telephone was invented by Alexander Graham Bell.
Sir Arthur Conan Doyle invented the character, Sherlock Holmes.	
	The play, *Henry the Fifth*, was written by Shakespeare.

Extension

Either:

- Write a paragraph about a famous inventor of the 19th century (using mainly the active voice).

Or:

- Write a paragraph about some famous inventions of the 19th century (using mainly the passive voice).

Dear Helper,

Objective: to find out more about active and passive verbs.

Help your child to see how, very often, in changing sentences from active to passive, the 'doer' follows the verb (the action word) and the object to whom something is done precedes the verb.

Majestic trouble

- Read the notice.
- Make a list of difficult words and look up their meaning in a dictionary.

NOTICE

In 1999 items from the wreck of the liner *Majestic* (sunk by enemy action in 1942) were recovered by an international deep-sea exploration team and landed in Porto Paso harbour.

Pursuant to its laws, the government of Porto Paso is applying the procedure which allows surviving passengers or their assigns to claim these items.

Interested persons should contact:

Porto Paso Embassy   or: Government House
Regent Terrace   The Piazza
London W1   Porto Paso
UK   Tel. +987 654 321
Tel. 0123 456789

They will be sent a list of all the items and a form on which to make a claim for restitution. They will also receive a leaflet detailing all necessary information about the procedure that must be followed and the evidence required to prove the claims.

Photographs of the items are available, but these cannot be sent by post. They must be inspected in person at one of the above locations.

Claimants are reminded that they must:

- establish proof of ownership
- contribute to the cost of recovering the items from the sea bed
- make their claim within a period of one year and a day from the date of publication of this notice.

- What is the notice about?
- What do you have to do if you wish to claim any of the items?

Extension

- Look through newspapers and magazines and find other examples of official notices for discussion.

Dear Helper,

Objective: to find out about formal language.

Official documents are often written in formal language which is difficult to understand. Your child is likely to encounter this in later life, so should become familiar with some of this more obscure language.

PHOTOCOPIABLE

Oily subjects

How to find the subject of a sentence in three easy steps

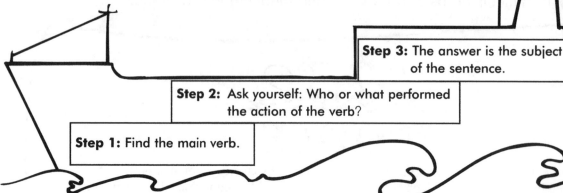

Step 3: The answer is the subject of the sentence.

Step 2: Ask yourself: Who or what performed the action of the verb?

Step 1: Find the main verb.

- Now, underline the **main verb** in one colour and the **subject** in another colour in these sentences.

The Exxon Valdez ran aground on a reef in Prince William Sound Alaska.

The oil leakage went on for two days.

260 000 barrels of oil poured into the sea.

Thousands of birds were killed.

Because of the slow response of the Exxon oil company, the oil slick spread for over 1000 miles.

Because of the damage to marine life, Alaska's fishing industry suffered badly.

The captain of the Exxon Valdez, who had a history of alchoholism, lost his job as a result of the disaster.

Fines totalling over 600 million pounds sterling were paid by the Exxon oil company.

Dear Helper,

Objective: to find the main subject and verb in a sentence.
Analysing sentences helps children to see how they are constructed. This aids their understanding of complex sentences in reading and enables them to be more adventurous in their own writing.

It's all relative

Relative pronouns introduce clauses which tell you more about a noun. In the sentence:
The dragon who lived in the dungeon was fierce.
who begins the clause 'who lived in the dungeon' which provides extra information about the dragon.
Other relative pronouns include **which, that, whose, whom.**

● Now, read the passage below and insert the correct relative pronoun in each of the gaps. It's easy! Just use your common sense – though the last one will need a little more thought.

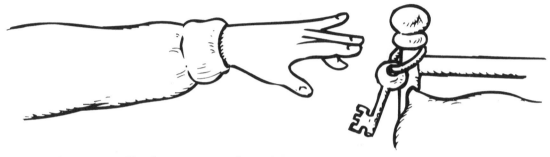

Solution to Hildebrand's dungeons adventure game

Go to the kitchen and take the MEAT _____ you will find on the table. There is also a SILVER KNIFE _____ will come in handy if you bump into the werewolf. Next, go to Hildebrand's bedroom and take the KEY _____ you will find hanging from his bed – but watch out! Hildebrand is the type of man _____ gets very angry if he finds you messing about with his things! Next, you must go to the laboratory and take the POISON _____ you will find in a retort on the workbench. Use this to poison the MEAT. Though not necessary, it is wise to go to the music room and take the LUTE from the ghost _____ you will find there. This will protect you from the monster _____ main aim in life is to roam the dungeons searching for something tasty to eat. You are now ready to try to rescue Madeline _____ is chained in a locked dungeon. Use the KEY _____ you got from the bedroom to unlock the door, then throw the poisoned MEAT to the hounds _____ are guarding Madeline. The POISON will soon kill them. You can then use the KEY to unlock Madeline, from _____ you will receive a generous reward.

Dear Helper,

Objective: to identify and understand the use of relative pronouns.
If necessary, remind your child that a pronoun is a word that stands in for a noun (eg *he, she, it*) which has previously been mentioned. In the example above, 'who' stands for 'the dragon'.

Talk, talk

When writing dialogue, remember to:
- Begin with speech marks and a capital letter.
- End with a comma, exclamation mark or question mark, followed by the closing speech marks.
- Begin a new indented line for every change of speaker.

Example:

'What time is it?' asked Stephen.
'How should I know?' replied Tony. 'It's pitch dark and I can't see my watch.'
'Use the torch. It's over there somewhere.'

- Now, punctuate these four passages.

1 Let me tell your fortune, said Alex. You can't tell fortunes! replied Andy. Yes I can, said Alex confidently. How? It's easy. It's all in this book!

2 John dashed through the door. Has the match started on TV yet? he asked his dad. No, they're just chatting. Bring me my drink John. Where is it? said John crossly. Where it always is, in the fridge.

3 have you seen Dave's bike asked one of the girls leaning against the wall yeah he's been riding it through the woods all afternoon I answered haven't you seen him no my mum kept me in to wash the dishes replied the girl.

4 what have you got on your feet said the teacher shoes said Chloe shoes exclaimed the teacher they look more like boots to me they're the latest fashion explained Chloe yes said the teacher for mountaineering

Dear Helper,

Objective: to revise the punctuation of dialogue.

The use of correct punctuation when writing dialogue is important because it indicates how a passage should be read or spoken. Read each dialogue aloud with your child, each taking a part. This will help to clarify how it should be punctuated.

Dash it!

A **dash** is used to:
- show additional information with more emphasis than a comma: eg 'He is a footballer – and a musician as well!'
- add extra information that shows a change of thought: eg 'I asked Susan – the prettiest girl in school – if she would give me a kiss.'
- indicate a pause, especially for effect: eg 'It was a wonderful holiday – the best.'

A **hyphen** is used to:
- link certain words: eg twenty-one, self-assurance, well-planned, north-east.
- indicate that a word has been split (usually in print) at the end of a line.
  Note that the split must be by syllable.

Note that a hyphen is usually shorter than a dash and has no space before or after it.
A dash is longer and has a space before and after it.

- Add **dashes** and **hyphens** to these sentences.

The self confidence of an actor comes from experience.

The government won a two thirds majority.

The beach was wonderful until it rained!

Our new teacher straight from college is great fun.

The self taught pianist played amazingly well.

Number twenty two in the charts is a remix of 'Fashion'.

His after school job left him tired in the mornings and that's an understatement!

Forty six thousand tons of ship takes a long time to slow down.

The last lifeboat *Collapsible B* was lowered.

They sent the distress signal QCD later they tried SOS.

Dear Helper,

Objective: to revise and practise the use of hyphens and dashes.

For more practice, look with your child for examples of the use of hyphens and dashes in books, magazines and newspapers. Try to identify how the punctuation is used in each case.

Beowulf, folk hero

- Summarise this story of Beowulf, the Anglo-Saxon folk hero, using no more than 100 words.

For twelve years, Hrothgar, King of Denmark, suffered while his kingdom was being ravaged by a devouring monster, named Grendel. Grendel's life was protected by a charm against all weapons forged by man. He lived in the wastelands and visited the hall of Hrothgar every night, carrying off and slaughtering many of the guests. Beowulf, hearing of Grendel's murderous visits, sailed from Geatland with fourteen brave companions to give Hrothgar his help.

Landing on the Danish coast, Beowulf was challenged as a spy. He persuaded the coastguards to let him pass, and he was received by King Hrothgar. When the king and his court retired for the night, Beowulf and his companions were left alone in the hall. All but Beowulf fell asleep. Then Grendel came. With one stroke he killed one of Beowulf's sleeping companions, but Beowulf, unarmed, wrestled with the monster and managed to tear Grendel's arm out at the shoulder. Grendel, mortally wounded, retreated, leaving a bloody trail from the hall to his lair.

The next night, Grendel's mother came to avenge the fatal injury to her monster son and carried off a Danish nobleman and Grendel's torn-off paw. Following the blood trail, Beowulf went to kill the mother. Armed with his sword, Hrunting, he came to the water's edge. He plunged in and swam to a chamber under the sea. There he fought with Grendel's mother and killed her. Nearby was Grendel's body. Beowulf cut off its head and brought it back as a trophy to King Hrothgar.

For fifty years Beowulf ruled his people in peace and serenity. Then suddenly a dragon, furious at having his treasure stolen from his hoard in a burial mound, began to ravage Beowulf's kingdom. Like Grendel, this monster left its den at night on its errand of murder and pillage. Beowulf, now an old man, resolved to fight the dragon alone. He approached the entrance to its den and strode forward shouting his defiance. The dragon came out, spluttering flames from its mouth. The monster rushed upon Beowulf with all its fury and almost crushed him in its first charge.

So fearful grew the struggle that all but one of Beowulf's men deserted and fled for their lives. Wiglaf remained to help his aged monarch. Another rush of the dragon shattered Beowulf's sword and the monster's fangs sunk into Beowulf's neck. Wiglaf, rushing into the struggle, helped the dying Beowulf to kill the dragon.

Dear Helper,

Objective: to practise the skill of summarising.

The skill of summarising requires a balance between decreasing the number of words while still retaining the basic meaning. Ask your child to read their summary to you. Have they managed to convey the gist of the story in roughly the amount of words required?

Italy

- Read this passage about Italy.
- Pick out ten key facts and jot them down in note form.
- Using your notes only, write a paragraph about Italy.

Italy is a country in the south of Europe. It has a land area of 301000 square kilometres and a population of 57 million people. It juts out into the Mediterranean Sea looking like a large boot which seems to be kicking a ball. The ball is the island of Sicily. Another large island, Sardinia, is also governed by Italy.

The boundary of Northern Italy is formed by the Alps. South of this is a fertile plain which includes farmlands and the big industrial towns of Turin and Milan. To the east is the historic city of Venice. Venice was built on a group of islands in a lagoon and the main streets are canals not roads. For this reason, Venice has remained unspoiled by modernisation, and is one of the world's most beautiful cities.

Further south is Rome. Rome is the capital city of Italy and one of the most famous and historic cities in the world. It was founded 2500 years ago, and became the capital of the Roman Empire which lasted until about 450 AD. Many of the ruins of ancient Rome, such as the Colliseum, are still a spectacular sight today. Rome is also famous for fine architecture of later periods. It is also the centre of the Roman Catholic Church.

The southern part of Italy, including the city of Naples, Sicily and Sardinia is known as the Mezzogiorno. The north has most of the business and industry, while the Mezzogiorno has most of the agriculture. As a result of this, 27% of people living in the south of Italy are below the poverty line, compared to only 3% in the north.

The climate of Italy is typically Mediterranean. It is hot and dry in the summer, and cool and wet in the winter. The highest average temperature for the Rome area is 26°C in August and the lowest is 11°C in January. Rainfall ranges from 70mm in January to 0mm in July.

The biggest issue for Italy in the 21st century is how to close the north-south divide. A range of ideas is being tried. These include developing industry and improving the infrastructure: roads, railways, telecommunications. Tourism is another area which could be developed. The south of Italy has a great deal to offer to tourists: hot weather, fine beaches, wonderful historic sites, for example, Pompeii and Paestum, and skiing on Mount Etna.

Dear Helper,

Objective: to practise the skill of note making.

Note making is a vital research and study skill which your child will use more and more as they progress into secondary school. Help your child to pick out the key fact or concept in each paragraph. This is often – but not always – contained in the first sentence (or topic sentence) of the paragraph.

PHOTOCOPIABLE

Be an editor

- Proofread this text for spelling mistakes.
- The text is also too wordy. Edit the text by finding words and phrases that could be deleted without losing important information.

The end of an era

A report on the birth of the computer and the decline of the typewriter

The first computer was desined in 1833 by the British mathematitian Charles Babbage. His design reqired more than 50 000 moving parts in a steam-driven machine as large as a locomotive. Just imagine having to stoke up a boiler before you could use your computer! Although Babbage worked on the analytical engine for nearly 40 years, he never made a working machine. Indeed, some people claim that it would not have been possible with the tecnology of the time, and the machine would have jamed as soon as it had been turned on. However, Babbage did construct severel smaller and simpler versions, examples of which can be seen at the Science Museum in London.

The first electronic computer, which used thermionic valves, was made in 1943. It was called 'Colossus' because of its size, and was used to brake German secret codes. However, Colossus can only perform the task it was designed for. The first general purpose electronic computer was ENIAC (which stands for Electronic Numerical Integrator and Calculator). It was 5 metres high, 24 metres long, and contained 800 kilometres of wiring. ENIAC's first task was to work out calculashuns for the hydrogen bomb. Although it could perform different tasks, this could only be acheived with difficulty – by rewiring the computer. Just imagine having to take out your soldiering iron and rewire your computer in order to change from a word procesor to a game!

The next big revolushun took place in 1971 when the American engineer Marcian Hoff invented the sillycon chip, which he called a microproccessor. The microprocessor is the basis of all modern computers. Now it seems that every six months we hear about a new microprocessor which is smaller and faster. On the hole this is a good thing, but it does mean that we have to keep paying to upgrade our computers, whereas a good mecanical typeriter used to last a lifetime!

Extension

- Summarise the text by highlighting the five main points.

Dear Helper,

Objective: to edit and summarise a piece of writing.

This type of activity provides a model which your child can follow in proofreading and editing their own writing. You can encourage your child to look, not only at cutting out specific words and phrases, but also at rewriting sentences in fewer words.

Name: _____

If

- Read this well-known poem which is, in effect, one long conditional sentence.

If you can keep your head when all about you
Are losing theirs and blaming it on you;
If you can trust yourself when all men doubt you,
But make allowance for their doubting too:
If you can wait and not be tired by waiting,
Or, being lied about, don't deal in lies,
Or being hated don't give way to hating,
And yet don't look too good, nor talk too wise;

If you can dream – and not make dreams your master;
If you can think – and not make thoughts your aim,
If you can meet with Triumph and Disaster
And treat those two impostors just the same:
If you can bear to hear the truth you've spoken
Twisted by knaves to make a trap for fools,
Or watch the things you gave your life to, broken,
And stoop and build 'em up with worn-out tools;

If you can make one heap of all your winnings
And risk it on one turn of pitch-and-toss,
And lose, and start again at your beginnings,
And never breathe a word about your loss:
If you can force your heart and nerve and sinew
To serve your turn long after they are gone,
And so hold on when there is nothing in you
Except the Will which says to them: "Hold on!"

If you can talk with crowds and keep your virtue,
Or walk with Kings – nor lose the common touch,
If neither foes nor loving friends can hurt you,
If all men count with you, but none too much:
If you can fill the unforgiving minute
With sixty seconds' worth of distance run,
Yours is the Earth and everything that's in it,
And – which is more – you'll be a Man, my son!

Rudyard Kipling

- Now write your own 'If' poem using the following pattern:

> If **I won the lottery, I would buy myself a car.**
>
> If _____, I would _____.
>
> If _____, I would _____.
>
> If _____, I would _____.
>
> If _____, I would _____.
>
> _____.

- Use one of the following lines for the ending – or make up your own:

'If' - one little word that makes so much difference!

If, if only, if.

If, If, If, If.

Never mind 'if', I'll do it anyway!

Dear Helper,

Objective: to explore sentence constructions which use 'if'.

'If' is the most common word that signals a conditional sentence. The 'if' part of the sentence sets up the condition upon which the main part of the sentence depends. Other words that signal condition are 'unless' ('Unless you come home now, ...') and 'should' ('Should you find the key,...).

School rules ok!

Modal verbs are used to help main verbs express a range of meanings, usually to do with possibility, permission and obligation. These are shown in the table below.
(Note: in the examples, the **modal verb** is in italics and the **main verb** is in bold type.)

Modal	Meaning	Example
can	it is possible, or you have permission to do something	You *can* **do** this if you try.
may	you have permission to do something	You *may* **open** the window.
must	you have to do something (obligation)	You *must* **wear** a tie.
will	future time, or you have to, or want to do something	I *will* **be** a famous scientist.
shall	as above, but less commonly used than it used to be	*Shall* we **go** to the library?

- Add an appropriate **modal verb** in the blanks of this letter to parents.

Dear Parent,

The following new rules _____ be introduced next term.

- In the morning, pupils_____wait outside until the 8.35 bell.

- If it is raining, pupils_____go straight to their classroom.

- Pupils_____wear the correct uniform.

- Pupils_____not wear jewellery, though girls_____wear studs in their ears.

- Pupils_____never run in the school building.

- Pupils_____bring their swimming costumes on Wednesday.

- Pupils who_____already swim 100 metres_____bring their costumes on Friday.

- Pupils_____behave at all times or they_____be kept in detention.

Extension

- Write some extra rules and underline the **modal verb** in one colour and the **main verb** in another.

Dear Helper,

Objective: to make sentences which use the words 'can', 'may', 'must', 'will' and 'shall' to express possibility, permission and obligation.

We use modal verbs all the time, so your child will be familiar with them. The aim of the activity is to show how these words add to and refine the meaning of the main verb. Other modal verbs which you might investigate with your child are: 'would', 'could', 'might'.

A Victorian vampire

Amelia was asleep in her room when she heard a strange noise outside. When she looked out of the window she saw a strange creature. It had a mass of untidy hair, glowing red eyes and long sharp teeth.

Many years ago a family of two brothers and their sister moved into a house called Croglin Low Hall. At first they were very happy, but one night something strange happened.

Next day they organised a search for the creature. In a tomb near the old church they found a coffin that had been opened. Inside the coffin was a body. It had long, untidy hair and long teeth. In its leg was a fresh bullet wound.

One of the brothers looked out of the window, and in the distance he saw the strange figure. He took his gun and shot at the creature. He hit the creature in the leg, but it managed to get away.

They burned the creature, and it never troubled them again.

She screamed, and her brother ran to help her, but by the time they got to her room it was too late. The creature had attacked her. It had bitten her throat and blood was streaming down her neck. Luckily, she was still alive.

- The paragraphs in this short story have been jumbled up. Read each paragraph separately, then cut them out, put them in the correct order and paste them on a new sheet of paper.

Extension

- Answer these questions.

How could you tell which paragraph was the beginning of the story?

How could you tell which paragraph was the end of the story?

What other clues helped you to put the paragraphs in order?

Dear Helper,

Objective: to understand how paragraphs in a short story are linked together.
Don't let your child rush straight into cutting and pasting. Read each paragraph with your child, then help them to find clues that will help to put the paragraphs in the correct order.

PHOTOCOPIABLE

Alien paragraphs

Writing a paragraph in fiction	Examples
Beginning New paragraphs may be started for: • a step forward in time • a flashback • a change of scene • a change of viewpoint • the introduction of a new character	Next day, the alien tried to communicate with his ship, but there was no reply. A girl walked into the laboratory and offered to help him. She seemed quite unafraid.
Development A paragraph is developed by: • descriptive detail • dialogue • a series of events	The girl's name was Helen. She was a laboratory assistant, not one of the scientists. By coming in to help the alien, she showed them all up with her courage and compassion.
Dialogue Set out with a new indented line for each speaker, like paragraphs. In the example opposite there are two speeches by two characters, but they are both part of the same paragraph which began with 'A girl... (see line 4).	'Don't be afraid,' she said. 'I'm here to help you. Tell me what you need.' 'I need a more powerful transmitter,' croaked the alien.

- Using the advice given above, write two more paragraphs about the alien.

Extension

- Complete the story about the alien or write a story on another topic. Follow the advice in the table.

Dear Helper,

Objective: to analyse how paragraphs are structured in fiction.
Help your child to understand the examples given in the explanation. Read it through with them and when your child has written part of the continuation, check that they are applying the guidance appropriately.

Venetian paragraphs

Writing a paragraph in non–fiction	Examples
A topic sentence This states what the paragraph is about. It is usually found at the beginning of a paragraph.	One of the most interesting places I have visited is Venice.
Development A paragraph is developed by: • adding details • stating facts • giving examples • relating an incident • giving reasons	Venice is a city in the north of Italy. It is interesting because it is built on islands in the Adriatic Sea. The easiest way to get around is by using boats called 'vaporetti' on the canals. It is impossible for cars to get to the centre of Venice, and for this reason it is totally unspoiled.
Concluding sentence This is the sentence that rounds off the paragraph.	Visiting Venice is like walking back in time.

• Use the examples above to write two paragraphs about interesting places you have visited.

Extension

• Turn the exercise into a carefully paragraphed essay entitled, 'Places'. Add an introductory paragraph, two or three more paragraphs about places you have visited and a concluding paragraph.

Dear Helper,

Objective: to analyse how paragraphs are structured in non-fiction texts.

Help your child understand the examples by reading it through with them. When your child has done part of the written task, check that each paragraph has a topic sentence and that it is developed using one or more of the ways shown. Above all, check that your child does not jump from one topic to another in the same paragraph.

Name:

You!

- Perform some of these poems with a friend or relative.
- Underline the repeated words or phrases.

I'm Just Going Out for a Moment

I'm just going out for a moment.
Why?
To make a cup of tea.
Why?
Because I'm thirsty.
Why?
Because it's hot.
Why?
Because the sun's shining.
Why?
Because it's summer.
Why?
Because that's when it is.
Why?
Why don't you stop saying why?
Why?

Michael Rosen

You!

You!
Your head is like a drum that is beaten for spirits.
You!
Your ears are like the fans used for blowing fires.
You!
Your nostril is like a mouse's den
You!
Your mouth is like a mound of mud.
You!
Your hands are like drum-sticks.
You!
Your belly is like a pot of rotten water.
You!
Your legs are like stakes.
You!
Your buttocks are like a mountain top.

Traditional Igbo

Will you remember me?

Will you remember me in a month?
 Of course!
Will you remember me in a year?
 Certainly.
Will you remember me in two years?
 Yes.
Will you remember me in three years?
 Of course!
Knock, knock.
 Who's there?
See, you've forgotten me already.

Anonymous

- Now, try writing your own short poem using repetition.

Dear Helper,

Objective: to recognise how poets use repetition of words or phrases in their poetry.
These poems work best when read aloud in pairs. Read them with your child, each of you taking a part.

Cargoes

Connotations are the subtle additional meanings which are suggested by a word's main meaning. For example, the word 'meadow' has **connotations** of green grass, cows, nature, and fresh air, while the word 'shed' has **connotations** of small, dark, stuffy and ramshackle. So, if you were advertising butter, would you say 'butter from the cows in our meadow', or 'butter from the cows in our shed'?

- Read the poem, **Cargoes.**

Cargoes

Quinquereme of Nineveh from distant Ophir
Rowin home to haven in sunny Palestine,
With a cargo of ivory,
And apes and peacocks,
Sandalwood, cedarwood, and sweet white wine.

Stately Spanish galleon coming from the Isthmus,
Dipping through the Tropics by the palm-green shores,
With a cargo of diamonds,
Emeralds, amethysts,
Topazes, and cinnamon, and gold moidores.

Dirty British coaster with a salt-caked smoke stack
Butting through the Channel in the mad March days,
With a cargo of Tyne coal
Road-rail, pig-lead,
Firewood, iron-ware, and cheap tin trays.

John Masefield

- Now, play a word association game with the words for the cargoes in each verse, eg 'ivory',' apes', 'peacocks', and so on. Say the word, then jot down the first two or three words which come into your head.
- Say the different connotations for the names of the ships and cargoes.
- What is the main contrast between verses 1 and 2 and verse 3?

Dear Helper,

Objective: to recognise how poets use words for associated ideas or images.
Play the association game with your child. Draw your child's attention to the fact that the connotations of 'cargoes' in the first two verses are beautiful and exotic, whereas those in the last verse are harsh and industrial.

PHOTOCOPIABLE

Very like a Whale

- Read this amusing poem.

One thing that literature would be greatly better for
Would be a more restricted employment by authors of simile and metaphor.
Authors of all races, be they Greeks, Romans, Teuton or Celts,
Can't seem just to say that anything is the thing it is but have to go out of their way to say
that is like something else.
What does it mean we are told
That the Assyrian came down like a wolf on the fold? In the first place,
George Gordon Byron had had enough experience
To know that it probably wasn't just one Assyrian, it was a lot of Assyrians.
However, as too many arguments are apt to induce apoplexy and thus hinder longevity,
We'll let it pass as one Assyrian for the sake of brevity.
Now then, this particular Assyrian, the one whose cohorts were gleaming in purple and gold,
just what does the poet mean when he says he came down like a wolf on the fold?
In heaven and earth more than is dreamed of in our philosophy there are a great many things,
But I don't imagine that among them there is a wolf with purple and gold cohorts or purple
and gold anythings.
No, no, Lord Byron, before I'll believe that this Assyrian was actually like a wolf I must have
some kind of proof;
Did he run on all fours and did he have a hairy tail and a big red mouth and big white teeth
and did he say Woof Woof?
Frankly I think it very unlikely, and all you were entitled to say, at the most,
Was that the Assyrian cohorts came down like a lot Assyrian cohorts about to destroy the
Hebrew host.
But that wasn't fancy enough for Lord Byron, oh dear me no, he had to invent a lot of figures
of speech and then interpolate them,
With the result that whenever you mention Old Testament soldiers to people they say Oh yes,
they're the ones that a lot of wolves dressed up in gold and people ate them.
That's the kind of thing that's being done all the time by poets, from Homer to Tennyson;
They're always comparing ladies to lilies and veal to venison,
And they always say things like that the snow is a white blanket after a winter storm.
Oh it is, is it, all right then, you sleep under a six-inch blanket of snow and I'll sleep under a
half-inch blanket of unpoetical blanket material and we'll see which one keep warm.
And after that maybe you'll begin to comprehend dimly
What I mean by too much metaphor and simile.

Ogden Nash

- What does Ogden Nash think about metaphors and similes?
- What does the poet use as an example of simile and metaphor?
- What do you think are the good points about metaphors and similes?
  Give some examples.

Dear Helper,

Objective: to recognise how poets use language to create images.
Your child will have learned that a *simile* is a comparison using 'like' or 'as', eg His wit is as sharp as a razor;
a *metaphor* is a direct comparison, eg His wit is a razor, cutting sharply. Remind them of the difference if necessary.

Swimming Swan

- Read these humorous poems aloud with a friend or an adult.
- Say what it is that makes each one funny. Look for: funny situations, alliteration, repetition, nonsense, bouncy rhythm, funny rhymes, tongue twisters.

Horrors

METHOUGHT I walked a dismal place
Dim horrors all around;
The air was thick with many a face
And black as night the ground.

I saw a monster come with speed,
Its face of grimmliest green,
On human beings used to feed,
Most dreadful to be seen.

I could not speak, I could not fly,
I fell down in that place,
I saw the monster's horrid eye
Come leering in my face!
Amidst my scarcely-stifled groans,
Amidst my moanings deep,
I heard a voice, "Wake! Mr. Jones,
You're screaming in your sleep!"

Lewis Carroll

A Limerick

A skeleton once in Khartoum
Invited a ghost to his room.
    They spent the whole night
    In the eeriest fight
As to who should be frightened of whom.

Anonymous

Swimming Swan

Swan swam over the sea,
Swim, swan, swim.
Swan swam back again,
Well swum, swan.

Anonymous

Reasons for Extinction

Dodos do
nothing to
dastards who do dodos down.

Dog-god does
not defend
dodos being undone.

Dodos lovey-dovey
with dodo darlings
don't become
dodo dams or dads.

Dodos do
dumb things like Dido or dinosaurs did.

So dodos die
out.   *H. O. Nazareth*

A Letter to Evelyn Baring

Thrippsy pillivinx,
    Inky tinky pobbleboskle abblesquabs? –
Flosky! beebul trimble flosky! – Okul
scratchabibblebongibo, viddle squabble tog-a-tog,
ferrymoyassity amsky flamsky ramsky damsky
crocklefether squiggs.
    Flinkwisty pomm,
            Slushypipp.
                    Edward Lear

A Clerihew

Sir Christopher Wren
Said, 'I am going to dine with some men.
If anybody calls
Say I'm designing St Paul's.'

Edmund Clerihew Bentley

Extension

- Try to find other examples of humorous poems or write one of your own!

Dear Helper,

Objective: to explore why humorous verse is funny.

It is sometimes difficult to say why something is funny. However, if children can explore the different ways poets use words to make them laugh, they can appreciate the craft in the writing and use it as a model for their own writing.

Two boys crying

- Read the poem.
- Alongside the description of each boy, explain how it makes you feel.
- Say what you think the message of the poem is and how the poet gets it across.

Two boys crying

Across the world
Two boys are crying
Both wanting more
And tired of trying.

The first boy wants a mountain bike
And blames his mum for being mean;
Had enough of the daily hike,
He's desperate to be part of the scene.
All day long
The wanting burns strong.
All the night
The wanting burns bright.
So little to ask,
Bikes are everywhere;
Oh, why is life so unfair?

The second boy wants something to eat
But is too weak to place the blame.
His mother weeps, helpless, dead-beat,
While his father hangs his head in shame.
All day long
The hunger burns strong.
All the night
The hunger burns bright.
So little to ask,
Food is everywhere;
Oh, why is life so unfair?

Across the world
Two boys are crying,
One's full of life,
The other is dying.

Ray Mather

Extension

- Write another verse, saying what you want.

Dear Helper,

Objective: to explore how messages, moods and feelings are conveyed in poetry.

Discuss the poem with your child and find out how they feel about each of the boys and the contrast between them. Share your own feelings about the poem.

Introducing Claire

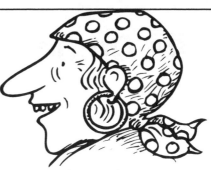

- Read this extract from a detective story.
- Highlight or underline the words and phrases which build up a description of Claire.

It could have been the inside of a gypsy caravan – a small, cluttered room, with a small round table in the middle, and on the table a crystal ball. A little old woman rose to greet me. She was wearing a long dress, a brightly-coloured headscarf, and a black silk shawl draped around her shoulders. At first she looked strange – frightening – but then a smile lit up her wrinkled face. She studied me carefully and her shrewd blue eyes glittered as though she knew already who I was and why I had come.

Why, indeed, had I come? Because the police had failed, because the most expensive private detective in London had failed – because I had no other choice.

'Are you Claire Voyant?' I asked hesitantly.

'That's what they call me,' she laughed. Her voice was unexpected. It was young and musical, with just the hint of a foreign accent, and seemed to belong to a different person than the one with the old wrinkled face. 'My real name is Clara Vonowski. Claire Voyant is just a nickname, though a highly appropriate one!'

'Do you think you can help me?' I enquired doubtfully.

'To find your daughter, you mean?'

I gasped. How could she know already what I wanted?

She laughed again. 'Don't look so surprised. I read the papers. I read about the mysterious disappearance three weeks ago – and I have an excellent memory.'

I relaxed a little. 'But how can you possibly help me to find a missing person when the police – with all their modern computers and databases – failed?'

Talk of computers and databases did not seem to impress her. 'I have the gift of second sight. It is a strange gift, I'll grant you, but not so strange as it might seem at first. Let me try to explain. You have heard of water diviners?'

'Yes, they find water with a stick split in a Y-shape.'

'Did you know that some diviners don't even need to walk over the field? They can find water with a pendulum held above a map.'

'I have heard something of the kind,' I mumbled uncertainly.

'Well, my gift is like that – only magnified.'

All at once, I felt relieved. I believed her and I knew that she could help me.

'All I need is something that belonged to Sally, and I think I will be able to tell you where she is. Rescuing her, however, will be a whole different kind of problem...'

From *"The Adventures of Claire Voyant"* by Agnes Kirsty

- Write a paragraph describing how Claire differs from the average detective.

Dear Helper,

Objective: to investigate the features of detective stories.

Help your child to pick out the words and phrases that describe Claire. Discuss how Claire is different from other detectives.

La Belle Dame Sans Merci

- Read this famous poem (written in 1819) by John Keats.

I.
O, what can ail thee, knight at arms,
    Alone and palely loitering?
The sedge has wither'd from the lake,
    And no birds sing.

II.
O, what can ail thee, knight at arms,
    So haggard and so woe begone?
The squirrel's granary is full,
    And the harvest's done.

III.
I see a lilly on thy brow,
    With anguish moist and fever dew;
And on thy cheeks a fading rose
    Fast withereth too.

IV.
I met a lady in the meads,
    Full beautiful a faery's child,
Her hair was long, her foot was light,
    And her eyes were wild.

V.
I made a garland for her head,
    And bracelets too, and fragrant zone;
She look'd at me as she did love,
    And made sweet moan.

VI.
I set her on my pacing steed,
    And nothing else saw all day long;
For sidelong would she bend, and sing
    A faery's song.

VII.
She found me roots of relish sweet,
    And honey wild, and manna dew,
And sure in language strange she said
    "I love thee true."

VIII.
She took me to her elfin grot,
    And there she wept and sigh'd full sore,
And there I shut her wild wild eyes
    With kisses four.

IX.
And there she lulled me asleep
    And there I dream'd Ah! woe betide!
The latest dream I ever dream'd
    On the cold hill side.

X.
I saw pale kings and princes too,
    Pale warriors, death pale were they all;
They cried "La Belle Dame sans Merci
    Hath thee in thrall!"

XI.
I saw their starv'd lips in the gloam,
    With horrid warning gaped wide,
And I awoke and found me here,
    On the cold hill's side.

XII.
And this is why I sojourn here
    Alone and palely loitering,
Though the sedge has wither'd from the lake,
    And no birds sing.

John Keats

- Write a summary of the story in the poem.
- Pick out some descriptions which you enjoyed and discuss with your helper why you liked them.

Dear Helper,

Objective: to read the poetry of an important poet of the past.
Share the reading with your child, perhaps reading alternate verses. Help your child to summarise the story and discuss your own favourite descriptions in the poem.

PHOTOCOPIABLE

Flashback planner

● Use this planner to plan a story with a flashback.

Exciting scene: Begin with the most exciting part of your story (which will probably be from somewhere in the middle of the story).

Flashback: The purpose of this is to describe the things which led up to the exciting scene. Think about how the flashback takes place: does the narrator (author) jump back in time, does the main character have a dream or tell another character?

Continuation: How does the story continue?

Ending: Plan the ending to your story. Can you link it to the exciting scene which you began with or to the flashback?

Dear Helper,

Objective: to write a story using the flashback technique.

Before planning a flashback story, your child will have read one at school. However, if you know of an example, you could share it with your child. The aim of the writing task is to convey time appropriately: starting at one point, going back in time, then moving forward again.

Name:

Crime cards

Crime Blackmail	**Crime** Burglary	**Crime** Fraud
Crime Mugging	**Crime** Murder	**Crime** Drug dealing
Crime Forgery	**Crime** Kidnapping	**Crime** Tax evasion

Alibi At a restaurant	**Alibi** At the cinema	**Alibi** Visiting aged grandparent
Alibi In a business meeting	**Alibi** At a party	**Alibi** With a girlfriend/boyfriend
Alibi On holiday	**Alibi** In prison	**Alibi** Abducted by aliens

- Cut out the two sets of cards: **Crime** and **Alibi**.
- Shuffle each pack and select one card from each at random. Then, make up a story to fit the crime and the alibi!

Dear Helper,

Objective: to use ideas cards to help write a detective story.
Do the activity along with your child, taking turns to think up ideas for a story. Then, your child can choose which they like best to work up into a written story.

100 LITERACY HOMEWORK ACTIVITIES • YEAR 6 TERM 2

Television troubles

- Read the arguments for and against the statement.
- Highlight the main points in each one (there are four in each passage).

Statement: Television is a harmful influence on young people.

For

Television is a harmful influence on young people because they spend too much time watching it. This means that homework does not get done, or is rushed, and that some young people stay up too late and are tired at school next day.

Another problem is that there is too much sex and violence on television which sets a bad example. Is it just a coincidence that there is far more crime and far more teenage pregnancies than in the 1950s when television was just beginning? When young people see all this sex and violence, they think it is the normal way to behave, and so the problem keeps growing.

Some people say that the educational programmes make television worthwhile, but in reality there are few programmes of educational value. If you look at a programme guide, you will see that 90% of a typical day's output is rubbish – cartoons, game shows, soap operas, movies and so on.

Finally, there is the problem of advertising. Advertising on television is so frequent that it is almost a form of brainwashing. It persuades people to spend their money on things they don't really want, or can't afford. Worse, it makes people envious of others when they see expensive items they can't have.

For these reasons, I think that television is a harmful influence on young people.

Against

Only people who are old-fashioned or out of touch could say that television is harmful to young people. Television is a 'window on the world' – it simply shows us what is 'out there' in different forms: news, soaps, documentaries and so on. This helps young people to learn about the complicated world they live in and how to cope with it.

Another important point is that there are a great many educational programmes on television ranging from programmes which help children to learn to read and write, to documentaries which examine important issues in detail. Some of the things we see on television could never be the same in a book. For example, a documentary on volcanoes can show us the sheer violence of an eruption as it actual happens – how much better than a diagram on a page!

Critics of television always talk about sex and violence, but sex and violence are part of our society and television can help us to cope with them. It can do this by providing information on sexually–transmitted diseases, self-defence, telling us which countries are safe to visit for holidays and so on.

Television is also the best way to keep up-to-date on current affairs. This is very important if we want to grow up to be adults who can play a full part in shaping our democratic society.

Finally, television provides valuable relaxation. In an age when stress is a problem for everyone, even school pupils, it can provide an important source of stress relief.

It is clear to me that anyone who thinks that television is a harmful influence is just trying to bury their head in the sand to escape from the real world.

- Write a summary of each argument in approximately 50 words.

Dear Helper,

Objective: to understand and summarise a balanced argument.

Help your child pick out the four main points in each argument. Discuss the issue, sharing your views.

Dolly debate

- Highlight the **facts** in this article in one colour and the **opinions** in another.

On 5th July 1996, at 5.00 p.m., Dolly was born. Dolly was the first animal to be created by a process called 'cloning'. Cloning is the process of creating groups of genetically identical cells. The cells themselves can be modified by adding DNA from any source. The process allows scientists to modify the genetic structure of any living thing, or to create perfect copies of any living thing.

Scientists claim that this knowledge will greatly improve medicine. For example, if the same ideas were applied to humans, it would be possible to regrow damaged limbs and organs. But is it wise to play god in this way? I think that, if we are not careful, we could end up with a world of Frankenstein monsters. Dr Frankenstein, you will remember, was a character in a story by Mary Shelley. He tried to create a perfect human being, but something went wrong, and he ended up with a monster.

Even if we avoid monsters, we could end up with 'designer' children. These would be created by mothers-to-be choosing from a 'shopping list' of genes: gender, eye colour, intelligence, build, artistic ability, and so on. I think this would be a disaster because it would go against the whole purpose of sexual reproduction which is to provide random variations of genes in case some are better fitted for survival.

We could end up with a world like the one described in Aldous Huxley's *Brave New World,* in which children are made in laboratories. If you read the book you will find out that it was not a very happy world. It would be a disaster if we made it come true!

We already have 'Frankenstein foods'. These are plants which have been genetically modified to be resistant to disease, to provide greater nutrition, and in some cases to grow bigger. But what will be the effects of eating them? I don't know about you, but I don't want to blow up like a balloon just because I have eaten some growth hormone! This danger has been realised, and genetically modified foods are now strictly controlled and have to be clearly labelled.

I believe that we will have to think very carefully about how we use the technology we develop in order to protect our future.

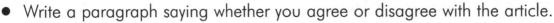

- Write a paragraph saying whether you agree or disagree with the article.
- Highlight your **facts** in one colour and your **opinions** in another.

Dear Helper,

Objective: to be able to distinguish personal opinion from fact.

Discuss the subject of the argument with your child, listening to their views and sharing yours. Can either of you think of any further facts to support your views?

Name:

The directions game

- Play this game with someone else.
- Take it in turns to give each other directions to get from one place to another. As the directions are given, follow them on the map.
- Write down some examples, like this:

From the Town Centre Tram Station to St Michael's Church
When you come out of the station, turn left into Keats Avenue. Walk along Keats Avenue until you get to High Street, then turn left again. Walk along High Street past the Youth Club and the bank. St Michael's Church is just after the bank.

Dear Helper,

Objective: to understand directions.

Take it in turns with your child to give and follow directions.

How to argue

- Study the table showing different ways of constructing an argument.
- Make a plan for an argument on a topic given to you by your teacher.

NOTE: do not try to use every kind of argument. Just choose the types of argument that suit your topic.

Constructing an argument	Examples
By giving an **example**	Yesterday, I saw a fox which had been killed by hounds. It had been ripped to pieces after a desperate flight for freedom.
By giving **facts or statistics**	Over 1000 foxes are killed in this cruel way every year.
By referring to **expert opinion**	The RSPCA say that the best way to control the fox population is by shooting, as this kills them quickly and painlessly.
By appealing to **emotions**	This is far better than a panic-stricken chase followed by being viciously bitten by hounds and dying in slow agony.
By appealing to **common sense**	Nowadays, if we want sport, there are thousands of harmless but exciting activities to choose from and if we want to control the fox population, this can be done humanely with guns. Fox-hunting is just not necessary.
By appealing to the **sense of right and wrong** or what is **fair.**	We all know that killing is wrong. Sadly, it is sometimes necessary to kill animals, but surely it can never be right to kill them just for fun – which is what the so-called sport of fox hunting is all about.
By using words which have **positive** or **negative connotations.**	Shooting foxes is sad, but at least it is humane. It is better than being slaughtered by hounds for sport.
By attacking your **opponents' arguments.**	The reason why fox hunters say that shooting is not the best way to control foxes is so that they can continue with their cruel sport.

Dear Helper,

Objective: to learn how to construct an argument.

Your child will have been given or chosen a topic on which to write. Discuss the topic together in order to gather ideas for developing a strong argument.

Be controversial

- Study the plan and the example below. Use the plan to write a balanced essay on a controversial issue.

Plan: use for any issue	Example: cloning
Introduction Write a paragraph in which you explain the issue. Give key names, dates and facts. Explain any difficult terms, eg 'cloning'.	Cloning is the process of creating groups of genetically identical cells. The cells themselves can be modified by adding DNA from any source. The process allows scientists to modify the genetic structure of any living thing, or to create perfect copies of any living thing.
One side of the issue Write at least two paragraphs giving evidence, examples or arguments to support one side of the issue.	This knowledge will greatly improve medicine. For example, babies could have their genes modified to protect against common diseases. It will also be possible to regrow damaged limbs and organs. Another advantage of cloning is that a new generation of plants can be created which will be resistant to disease and will provide greater nutrition.
Other side of the issue Write at least two paragraphs giving evidence, examples or arguments to support the other side of the issue.	The most serious argument against tampering with genes is that harmful bacteria might be produced by accident — indeed, some people believe that this is where AIDS came from (though this cannot be proved). Also, can we be sure that these new 'Frankenstein foods' will not affect our health? There is also a moral issue: is it right to tamper with the genetic material of living creatures — especially humans?
Conclusion State which of the above arguments you find most convincing; state which side of the issue you support.	This is a difficult issue, and I do think the dangers are very real. However, I do believe that we have to pursue these developments because of the good they can do. If scientists do this with very great care and with due respect for the moral issues, humanity will surely benefit overall.

Dear Helper,

Objective: to plan a balanced argument on a controversial issue.

Your child will have been given or chosen an issue on which to write. Discuss the issue together in order to help him or her gather ideas for both sides of the argument — and finally to decide which side of the argument to support.

Spelling guide

- Write a spelling guide for younger children using the headings below.
  - Explain the rules or give helpful tips, where appropriate.
  - Give some examples.
  - Add any other rules which you think are important on the other side of the sheet.

Rules and tips	Examples
i before **e**	
ful/less suffixes	
ed/ing suffixes	
y/ies plurals	
f/ves plurals	
irregular plurals	
words with silent letters	

Dear Helper,

Objective: to revise spelling knowledge.

Writing a spelling guide for younger children will demonstrate your child's own knowledge of spelling rules. Remind them that there are always exceptions to spelling rules. And, sometimes there are no rules for difficult and tricky spellings – they just have to be learned!

New word generator

New words are being created all the time to describe new inventions and ideas.

- Choose a **prefix** and a **word**, or a **word** and a **suffix**, or even all three – a **prefix**, **word** and **suffix** – to invent a new word.

- Invent an object to suit the new word and describe it, for example:
  new word = biocatalogue   object = catalogue of life forms

Prefix	Word	Suffix
anti-	brain	-able
bio-	catalogue	-a-gram
cyber-	chip	-aholic
desktop-	computer	-athon
e-	consumer	-cred
euro-	environment	-drivel
hyper-	gorilla	-friendly
inter-	kiss	-hostile
net-	language	-modernist
mega-	mail	-ocrat
micro-	market	-ofear
multi-	media	-space
street-	ozone	-speak
super-	star	-struck
techno-	street	-technology
tele-	television	-trendy
web-	video	-zine

- Add your own prefixes, words and suffixes:

Dear Helper,

Objective: to invent new words using known words and adding prefixes and suffixes.

This is a fun activity which can be easily shared. If necessary, remind your child of the following definitions: a *root* is the basic part of a word to which other parts can be added to change the meaning – a *prefix* at the beginning and a *suffix* at the end.

Word games

Word chains

A word chain is made by changing one letter at a time. Here is an example:

(mean)-(bean)-(beat)-(best)-(pest)-(post)-(port)-(part)-(park)-(bark)-(barn)

- Add more words to this chain.
- Start your own word chain.

Anagrams

- Find the names in each of these jumble of letters.

  noriam   lliawim   risch

  yarm   nasus   loctharte

- Make up an anagram of your name and names of your friends or family.

Alphabet words

- Think of an animal name for each letter of the alphabet. Here are a few to start.

  ape   bird   cat   dog   eel

Crosswords

- Look at the crossword below. The main word is written downwards and, across are words on the same subject.

field	c	h
tractor	o	o
ram	m	l
meadow	p	i
ewe	u	d
cart	t	a
	e	y
	r	

- Write similar crosswords for the other two words.

Dear Helper,

Objective: to extend vocabulary by playing words games.
Word games of all sorts are an excellent way of improving spelling and developing vocabulary and should be encouraged. The games on this sheet can be played at any time by children of all abilities.

A handsome beast

- Each verse of this poem describes an animal. Guess as many as you can.
- Add more verses to the poem or write some riddles on another subject.

A handsome beast and rather shy
It sounds a very costly buy.

He's at a cricket match always
But prefers the nights over the days.

He's not intentionally rude
Although it sounds as if he's nude.

We're told we know what sailors are
Well, here's a very backward tar.

He likes the hot and sunny weather
For putting two plus two together.

It sounds as if this creature's plight is
Suffering from laryngitis.

A creature judging by the sound
With which the human head is crowned.

Some are small and some are whoppers
A form of transport used by coppers.

You'll find him at the London Zoo
He's black and white and walked on too.

Dear Helper,

Objective: to extend vocabulary by guessing and writing riddles.

Children can learn a great deal about language by playing with it. Riddles are a very ancient form of language play and these, written in rhyme, have a format that can be easily copied. Help your child to guess the answers and to write some more verses.

As blind as a bat

Here are some **similes** that are used so often they have become tired **clichés**.
● Write new versions of each one. The first one is done as an example.

as blind as a bat	as blind as a new-born mouse
as brave as a lion	
as busy as a bee	
as cunning as a fox	
as gentle as a dove	
as graceful as a swan	
as hairy as a gorilla	
as heavy as an elephant	
as stubborn as a mule	
as playful as a kitten	
as poor as a church mouse	
as proud as a peacock	
as slow as a tortoise	
as strong as an ox	
as timid as a mouse	
as wise as an owl	

Dear Helper,

Objective: to create some original comparisons.

Remind your child that a *simile* is a comparison of two things using the words, 'like' or 'as'. A *cliché* is an over-used expression. *Similes* help authors and poets create images in the reader's mind. Encourage originality. Keeping to the animal theme might be difficult, but worth a try!

Your eyes are like...

- Follow the instructions and use the grid below
  to write a poem with some really imaginative similes.
  You will also need a dice.

Step 1

- Roll a dice to select an **object** from the grid.
- Roll again to select a **comparison** from the grid.
- Use the comparison to write an effective **simile**, as in these examples.
  Notice how each comparison is explained as fully as possible.

Examples:

Your eyes are like computer monitors
because they glow with a radiant blue
and I just love looking into them
because they are more lively than
my best computer game.

Your hair is like a mobile phone
because it is stylish and up-to-date
and I just love its many features
because they send strong signals and
communicate so much about you.

object	comparison	my objects
1 eyes	1 box of chocolates	1
2 hair	2 computer monitor(s)	2
3 ears	3 electric guitar(s)	3
4 lips	4 mobile phone(s)	4
5 nose	5 pencil sharpener(s)	5
6 voice	6 pizza(s)	6
Pattern:		

Your _____ is/are like (a/an) _____ because _____ .

Step 2

- Write any six objects in the 'my objects' column on the grid and follow the same process.

Step 3

- Pick out some of your best similes and use them to write a poem. Break up long lines into short lines like a free-verse poem, as in the examples above.

Dear Helper,

Objective: to create imaginative comparisons.
Remind your child that a simile is a comparison of two things using the words 'like' or 'as'. Help your child to think of imaginative and relevant ways that the subject is like the object of the comparison.

PHOTOCOPIABLE

Weregirl

- Read this example of narrative text. Put examples of the key features of narrative text in the appropriate space on the grid.

It all began one day last December. It had been a typical boring day at school and, when I got home, I was feeling moody and bad-tempered. Well, there's nothing so unusual in that, but I was feeling all hot and itchy as well. Straight after tea I ran upstairs and got in the bath.

At first, the hot water made me feel better. I lay back and massaged the soapy bubbles into my tired skin. Through the window I could see the moon, which had just risen. It was a full moon and so bright that it made me feel dizzy.

Then the itching came back again. My legs were the worst. I scratched and scratched. Then I looked at them. They were bright red and – horror – they were hairy! I don't mean hairy like a gorilla, but hairy like...like...well, like a man. But I'm only ten and my skin is as smooth as a baby's bottom – usually.

Features of narrative text	Example
Subjects Narratives (stories) can be on any subjects. Popular categories (genres) include: adventure, crime, fantasy, horror, romance, science fiction, historical fiction.	
Types of text Stories can be told in many forms: eg novels, short stories, poems, plays (stage, film, radio, TV).	
Organisation Narrative texts are usually chronological. Written texts are divided into paragraphs (usually marked by indentations) and chapters. Illustrations may be found, but are not essential.	
Language Novels and short stories are usually written in the past tense. Use of direct speech is common. Characters and settings are often described in detail. Playscripts are usually written in the present tense.	

- Find another example of narrative text and analyse it in the same way.

Dear Helper,

Objective: to revise the features of narrative texts.

Not all stories will conform to the features outlined here. If the example your child chooses does not, discuss how and why.

Hengest

- Read this example of recount text.
- Put examples of the key features of recount text in the appropriate space on the grid.

Hengest came to Britain in 449 AD with about three hundred men in three longships. They had been hired by Vortigern, the king of Britain, to help him fight off the Picts, who were invading Britain from the North. They did defeat the Picts and, afterwards, Vortigern gave Hengest and his men rewards of money and land.

Unfortunately, they wanted more and rebelled against him. Many battles were fought, but eventually Vortigern was defeated and retreated to a castle in Wales.

Then, another member of the British royal family, Aurelius Ambrosius, raised an army in Brittany and marched against Hengest. He fought a great battle, near Conisbrough Castle in Yorkshire, at which Hengest was killed.

Features of recount text	Example
Subjects Recount texts are often about people and events. Categories include: biographies, autobiographies, historical accounts, travel accounts.	
Types of text Recounts come in a variety of forms: eg reference books, encyclopaedia entries, diaries, film and TV documentaries.	
Organisation Recounts are organised in chronological order and often include an introduction to orientate or guide the reader. Written recounts are organised by paragraphs (note that *block* paragraphs are often used) and chapters. Illustrations may be included.	
Language Recounts are written in the past tense and use time connectives to link ideas and paragraphs. They may be written in a formal or informal language.	

- Find another example of recount text and analyse it in the same way.

Dear Helper,

Objective: to revise the features of recount texts.

Not all recounts will conform to the features outlined here. If the example your child chooses does not, discuss how and why.

Name:

Asteroid blaster

- Read this example of instructions text.
- Put examples of the key features of instructions text in the appropriate space on the grid.

Installation of 'asteroid blaster'

'Asteroid Blaster' can be run from Windows. The following procedure can be used to install the product:

1 Place the CD into your CD ROM drive.
2 Go to the Control Panel (Start/Settings/Control Panel).
3 Double click 'Add/Remove Programs'.
4 Follow the on-screen instructions.

Enjoy your game!

Features of instructions text	Example
Subjects Categories for instructions include: technical information, assembly instructions, rules, etiquette, directions, recipes.	
Types of text Instructions can be written in a variety of forms: from a simple poster to a thick computer manual.	
Organisation The step-by-step nature of instructions is often made clearer by numbers or bullet points. Diagrams are common and are sometimes essential.	
Language Instructions are written in clear, imperative sentences that tell the reader what to do. The language used is usually the bare minimum to make the procedure easy to follow. Prepositions are a feature to tell the reader where components or ingredients used are placed or arranged.	

- Find another example of instructions text and analyse it in the same way.

Dear Helper,

Objective: to revise the features of instructions texts.

Not all instructions will conform to the features outlined here. If the example your child chooses does not, discuss how and why.

In the Atlantic

- Read this example of report text.
- Put examples of the key features of report text in the appropriate space on the grid.

Procedure
We placed two beakers of water above a large bowl of water. The water in the beakers was at body temperature and a thermometer was placed in each one. One of the beakers was lowered into the bowl of water. The temperatures shown on the thermometers were recorded every two minutes and plotted on a graph.

Result
The temperature of the water in the beaker placed in the bowl of water went down the faster.

Conclusion
This proves that the people from the *Titanic* who went into the water would lose body heat faster than those in the lifeboats.

Features of report text	Example
Subjects Report texts present things as they are. They can be about a variety of subjects. Categories include: science research, quality control information in business, technical data, educational performance.	
Types of text Reports have a special format, eg school, science experiments, police reports.	
Organisation Report texts are often organised under subheadings, eg a school report is organised by subjects. They can include tables, graphs or diagrams.	
Language Reports use precise language, including data such as facts and figures. The passive voice is used to keep the tone impersonal. Reports can be in the past or present tense.	

- Find another example of a report text and analyse it in the same way.

Dear Helper,

Objective: to revise the features of reports.

Not all reports will conform to the features outlined here. If the example your child chooses does not, discuss how and why.

PHOTOCOPIABLE

The steam engine

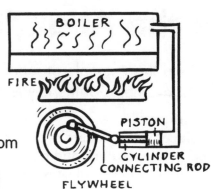

- Read this example of explanation text.
- Put examples of the key features of explanation text in the appropriate space on the grid.

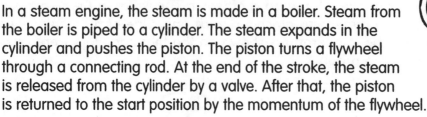

In a steam engine, the steam is made in a boiler. Steam from the boiler is piped to a cylinder. The steam expands in the cylinder and pushes the piston. The piston turns a flywheel through a connecting rod. At the end of the stroke, the steam is released from the cylinder by a valve. After that, the piston is returned to the start position by the momentum of the flywheel.

Features of explanation text	Example
Subjects Explanations can be about anything that a reader needs to understand. Categories include: scientific, technical, historical, geographical, general information.	
Types of text Formats for explanations include: encyclopaedia entries, reference books, manuals.	
Organisation Explanatory texts can be chronological or non chronological. The text is often linked to pictures or diagrams which make the explanations clearer. Often, the pictures or diagrams are essential to understanding the explanation.	
Language Explanations are usually written in an impersonal style and in the present tense. Connectives, particularly those of time and place are used to link procedures, sequences and cause and effect. Technical words and terms are an important feature of explanatory texts.	

- Find another example of an explanation text and analyse it in the same way.

Dear Helper,

Objective: to revise the features of explanation texts.
Not all explanations will conform to the features outlined here. If the example your child chooses does not, discuss how and why.

Capital punishment

- Read this example of persuasive text.
- Put examples of the key features of persuasive text in the appropriate space on the grid.

Capital punishment means punishment by death: by hanging, electric chair, garotte or any other method. In Britain, it was abolished in 1964, but there are many people, including several leading politicans, who would like to see it brought back.

However, there is no conclusive evidence to show that the death penalty is a more effective deterrent than life imprisonment. Another reason why the death penalty should not be brought back is that there is always the risk of executing innocent people. Many people believed this happened in the case of Everett Applegate, who was sent to the electric chair in 1936 on the basis of uncorroborated testimony. Other examples are Wayne Spence, killed in 1982 and Roy Roberts, killed in 1999. Civilised society should not need to resort to something so barbaric as the death penalty.

Features of persuasive text	Example
Subjects The subject of persuasive and discursive texts can be any debatable issue, eg capital punishment, environment. Persuasive texts argue for one side of an issue; discursive texts explore both sides.	
Types of text Formats can vary. They include: advertisements, leaflets, articles, documentary programmes, debate speeches.	
Organisation Written texts begin with an explanation of the issue followed by a series of arguments. Advertisements and leaflets add important visual material. Persuasive/discursive texts are non-chronological as the arguments can be in any order.	
Language Persuasive/discursive texts are written in the present tense, using connectives to link and modify arguments. Examples, quotes, facts and statistics are used.	

- Find another example of a persuasive or discursive text and analyse it in the same way.

Dear Helper,

Objective: to revise the features of persuasive and discursive texts.

Not all persuasive and discursive texts will conform to the features outlined here. If the example your child chooses does not, discuss how and why.

Me and my girl

- Read this example of cockney rhyming slang from the play 'Me and My Girl'. If you read it carefully, you will see that every piece of slang is explained.
- Write an alphabetical glossary of the slang.

Duchess: I hope you enjoyed your drive.

Bill: Not arf—but I nearly lost me titfa!

All: Titfa?

Bill: Me tit for tat.

All: Tit for tat?

Bill: My hat! It was so windy I had to pull it over my gingerbread.

All: Gingerbread?

Bill: Me lump o' lead!

All: Lump of lead?

Bill: Me Uncle Ned!

All: Uncle Ned?

Bill: Oh, me 'ead—the empty part o' me.

Bill: I'm 'ere ter day an' gorne termorrer. I started loife wi nuffink an' I still got it; but when I'm absolutely 'earts –

Sir John: Arts?

Bill: 'earts of Oak.

Sir John: A Building Society?

Bill: Naow! Broke!

Bill: You're not kiddin' me, are yeh? D'you reely mean teh say as Lord Hareford were reely moi ole' pot an' pan?

Duchess: Pot and pan?

Bill: I mean – moi ole man. My farver ... I don't fit in ... 'Oxton 'stead of Oxford! 'Ere, I'm a sport. Gimme da bees an' honey.

All: Bees and honey?

Bill: The money – then I'll puff.

All: Puff?

Bill: Puff and blow!

Sir John: Why? Are you out of breath?

Bill: Naow! I mean – GO!

- Make a glossary of local slang words.

PHOTOCOPIABLE

Dear Helper,

Objective: to investigate rhyming slang.

We all use slang. It's just one of the ways we play with language in an informal way. Slang is often associated with certain regions. Cockney rhyming slang comes from the East End of London. Read this dialogue with your child, each taking a part.

Name:

S

Mini-zapper

Here are two letters in reply to a query about adapting an electronic keyboard.
One is formal and the other is informal.

- Make a list of the differences between the two. Look for: **language and style** eg
  length of words and sentences, **types of greeting** and **closure**, **tone**
  eg use of contractions.

Formal: a business letter from the Customer Services Manager.

```
Dear Mr Willis

Thank you for your enquiry. Our engineer has informed us that it is
possible to connect an external amplifier to your ACE 'MINI-ZAPPER'
KEYBOARD even though an external jack socket is not included with this
model.

Please note that undertaking this operation yourself will invalidate the
guarantee. We therefore recommend that you contact our Engineering
Department who will be pleased to do the work for you for an appropriate
fee.

The Engineering Department may be contacted on extension 217.

We trust this information has been of service to you. Please do not
hesitate to contact us again should you require further information.

Yours sincerely

I M Boss
Customer Services Manager
```

Informal: a note from a friend who works in the Engineering Department

Hi Bob,

It's easy to connect your Mini-Zapper to an amp – but you'll have to fit a jack socket. If you
do it yourself, you may as well tear up the guarantee, but send it to me at the engineering
department and we'll do it for you. Of course, we'll have to charge you for the work, but it
won't cost much. Call me on extension 217 – and don't forget to get in touch any time you
need help.

Cheers,

Dave

Dear Helper,

Objective: to compare formal and informal styles of writing.

Remind your child that formal and informal styles of writing are not a question of right and wrong, but
of what's appropriate for the particular purpose. If Dave wrote to his friend Bob in a formal way, he would
sound pompous. If the Customer Services Manager wrote informally, Bob might query the reliability of his
company to do a good job.

PHOTOCOPIABLE

Make it more complex!

- Experiment with the following methods of combining statements into complex sentences. Write your own examples in the boxes.

Using a **relative pronoun** (who, which, whose).

Examples:
I've got a little puppy whose name is Poppy.
The programme which I told you about is on TV tonight.

Using a **preposition + which** (at which, of which, to which, in which, on which).

Examples:
The chair on which you are sitting has just been painted.
Nearby is a cliff, beneath which you will find the cave.

Using the **past participle** (the past participle of regular verbs end in -ed).

Examples:
Assisted by a helpful youth, the old lady climbed the stairs.
Battered by wind and waves, the ship was a wreck.

Dear Helper,

Objective: to revise different ways of making complex sentences.
The complexity of sentences is a feature of the development of children's writing. Help your child to think of more examples of their own.

Name:

Hansel and Gretel

● Read this well-known fairy tale, told in a series of short, simple sentences.

Hansel and Gretel went for a walk in the woods. They dropped a trail of breadcrumbs to show the way back. The birds ate the breadcrumbs. They got lost. Soon they were hungry. They came to a house. It was made of sweets and chocolate. An old woman lived there. She caught them. She put them in a cage. She began to heat up her oven. She planned to eat them. Hansel escaped. He pushed the old lady into the oven. She was cooked instead!

● Expand the story to make it more interesting. Add descriptive words, phrases and clauses, and join the simple sentences in different ways to make more varied, complex ones. A start has been made for you.

Once upon a time, Hansel and Gretel, who were the children of a poor woodcutter, went for a walk in the deep, dark woods.

(continue on back)

Dear Helper,

Objective: to make a story more interesting by adding descriptive detail and varying the length and complexity of the sentences.

Help your child to expand the simple version of the fairy tale. It may help to tell the story orally first and then write it down.

Name:

Novel template

- Use this template to help you to write about a novel you have read and studied.

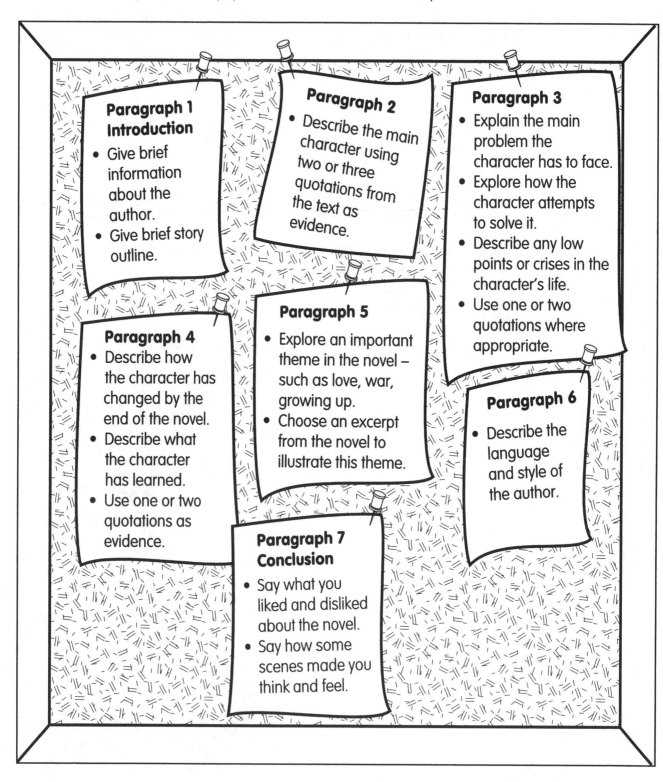

**Paragraph 1
Introduction**
- Give brief information about the author.
- Give brief story outline.

Paragraph 2
- Describe the main character using two or three quotations from the text as evidence.

Paragraph 3
- Explain the main problem the character has to face.
- Explore how the character attempts to solve it.
- Describe any low points or crises in the character's life.
- Use one or two quotations where appropriate.

Paragraph 4
- Describe how the character has changed by the end of the novel.
- Describe what the character has learned.
- Use one or two quotations as evidence.

Paragraph 5
- Explore an important theme in the novel – such as love, war, growing up.
- Choose an excerpt from the novel to illustrate this theme.

Paragraph 6
- Describe the language and style of the author.

**Paragraph 7
Conclusion**
- Say what you liked and disliked about the novel.
- Say how some scenes made you think and feel.

Dear Helper,

Objective: to write about a book which has been read and studied.

This sheet provides a model for writing an essay about a book. The word 'essay' sounds a bit daunting, but it is simply a piece of *organised* writing. Encourage your child to tackle one paragraph at a time.

100 LITERACY HOMEWORK ACTIVITIES • YEAR 6 TERM 3

Lost and found

William Blake (1757–1831) wrote many poems which are linked. Here are two of them.

- Read the poems, then answer the questions below.

The Little Boy Lost

'Father, father where are you going?
Oh do not walk so fast.
Speak father, speak to your little boy,
Or else I shall be lost.'

The night was dark, no father was there,
The child was wet with dew.
The mire was deep, and the child did weep,
And away the vapour flew.

The Little Boy Found

The little boy lost in the lonely fen,
Led by the wand'ring light,
Began to cry, but God ever nigh
Appeared like his father in white.

He kissed the child and by the hand led,
And to his mother brought,
Who in sorrow pate through the lonely dale
Her little boy weeping sought.

- Why does the little boy get lost?
- What is the boy's situation at the end of the poem?
- How does the boy come to be found?
- Give your explanation of what might have happened.
- What is the link between these two poems?

Dear Helper,

Objective: to explore two poems which are linked.

Read the poems with your child. Discuss your child's answers to the questions – and offer yours up for discussion, if they are different.

Poet-o-meter

- Read the poem given to you by your teacher into the 'microphone' of the poet–o–meter. Then, fill in the various 'read outs'.

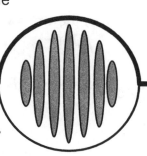

**Microphone
Read poem into here.**

Subject of poem: Colour in the LED to show how much you liked it. Write a brief summary below.

5		Gripping!
4		Pretty good
3		OK
2		Not bad
1		Boring

Verse form: Tick the boxes to show which features are used and describe them below.

	Rhyme
	Rhythm
	Free verse
	Long lines
	Short lines

Figurative language: Count each type of figure of speech and write one number in each of the boxes opposite. Write the best example below.

	Simile
	Metaphor
	Personification

Recommendation: Colour in the LED opposite and write your recommendation below.

5		Highly recommended
4		Recommended
3		OK
2		If you've nothing better to do
1		Don't bother

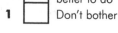

Dear Helper,

Objective: to read a poem and evaluate the style of the poet.
Encourage your child to read the poem aloud to you. Discuss the poem, offering your response and evaluation too.

The schoolboy

● Read this poem. Then, give your response opposite each verse.

I love to rise in a summer morn,
When the birds sing on every tree;
The distant huntsman winds his horn,
And the skylark sings with me.
Oh! What sweet company.

Explain how you feel on a beautiful summer morning.

But to go to school in a summer morn,
Oh! it drives all joy away;
Under a cruel eye outworn,
The little ones spend the day
In sighing and dismay.

Explain your feelings about going to school.

Ah! Then at times I drooping sit,
And spend many an anxious hour,
Nor in my book can I take delight,
Nor sit in learning's bower,
Worn through with the dreary shower.

How do your lessons make you feel?

How can the bird that is born for joy
Sit in a cage and sing?
How can a child when fears annoy
But droop his tender wing,
And forget his youthful spring?

What figure of speech does Blake use in this verse to describe a child at school?

O father and mother! if buds are nipped,
And blossoms blown away,
And if the tender plants are stripped
Of their joy in the springing day,
By sorrow and care's dismay,

Think of a figure of speech to explain how you feel about school.

How shall the summer arise in joy,
Or the summer fruits appear?
Or how shall we gather what griefs destroy,
Or bless the mellowing year,
When the blasts of winter appear?

William Blake

What effect does Blake think this kind of education will have in later life?

What effect will your education have in later life?

Dear Helper,

Objective: to write about a poem.
The prompts opposite each verse will help your child to focus on the meaning in each verse. Talk about the poem with your child and share your own responses.

Memorable Fancies

- Read 'Memorable Fancies' by William Blake.
- Write a simplified version of it in your own words.
  (The footnotes will help you.)

The ancient tradition that the world will be consumed in fire at the end of six thousand years[1] is true, as I have heard from Hell.

For the cherub with his flaming sword is hereby commanded to leave his guard at the tree of life; and when he does, the whole creation will be consumed and appear infinite and holy, whereas it now appears finite[2] and corrupt.

The notion that man has a body distinct from his soul is to be expunged[3]; this I shall do by printing in the infernal method, by corrosives[4], which in Hell are salutary[5] and medicinal, melting apparent surfaces away, and displaying the infinite which was hid.

If the doors of perception were cleansed everything would appear to man as it is, infinite.

For man has closed himself up, till he sees all things through narrow chinks of his cavern.

Opposition is true friendship.

One Law for the Lion and Ox is Oppression.

For everything that lives is holy.

[1] The year 2000. [2] finite = has an end. [3] expunged = wiped out. [4] corrosives = acids. [5] salutary = beneficial.

- Compare 'Memorable Fancies' with some of Blake's poems. Note down some similarities and differences in the table.

	'Memorable Fancies'	Poems by Blake
Form		
Subject		
Language		

Dear Helper,

Objective: to compare and contrast different work by the same writer.

'Memorable Fancies' is imaginative, poetic prose. The language is difficult, so discuss it with your child.

Daphne and Britney

- Read these two poems.
- Make a list of similarities and contrasts. Look for: **subject matter, form, figures of speech, time, setting.**

My Daphne's hair is twisted gold

My Daphne's hair is twisted gold.
Bright stars a-piece her eyes do hold:
My Daphne's brow inthrones the Graces.
My Daphne's beauty stains all faces.
On Daphne's cheek grow rose and cherry,
On Daphne's lip a sweeter berry;
Daphne's snowy hand but touched does melt,
And then no heavenlier warmth is felt;
My Daphne's music charms all ears.
Fond am I thus to sing her praise;
These glories now are turned to bays.*

John Lyly (1554-1606)

* This is a reference to the myth of Daphne and Apollo. When Apollo pursued Daphne,
the gods protect her by turning her into a laurel bush (bay). In other words, Daphne does not return Lyly's love.

Britney Boogie-Woogie

Britney smiles prettily in her party mood:
She looks so drop-dead beautiful, it's spooky,
Her hair is gold, her lips are red like blood,
Her hips sway to the disco boogie-woogie.

I ask her if she'd like to dance with me,
(Though I'd rather play a football game than boogie)
She says, 'Get lost, I'm dancing, can't you see!'
Her hips sway to the disco boogie-woogie.

Her voice is more melodious than the band
Even when she's saying things that bug me.
I know she hates me, but I love to stand
And watch her do the disco boogie-woogie.

Shopping Trolley (1989)

Dear Helper,

Objective: to compare poems by different poets.
Both of these are love poems, although the second is a pop-song lyric. Read them with your child and help them to think of ways in which they are alike and different.

PHOTOCOPIABLE

Grimms' Beam

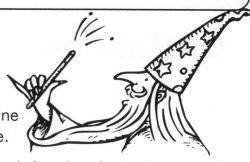

- Read this fairy tale.
- Compare it with others you have read and underline all the things that are typical of the fairy tale genre.

There was once a magician who was standing in the midst of a great crowd of people performing his wonders. He had a great bird brought in, which lifted a heavy beam and carried it as if it were as light as a feather. But a girl was present who had just found a bit of four-leaved clover, and had thus become so wise that no deception could stand out against her, and she saw that the beam was nothing but a straw. So she cried, "You people, do you not see that it is a straw that the bird is carrying, and no beam?" Immediately the enchantment vanished, and the people saw what it was, and drove the magician away in shame and disgrace. He, however, full of inward anger, said, "I will soon revenge myself."

After some time the girl's wedding-day came, and she was decked out, and went in a great procession over the fields to the place where the church was. All at once she came to a stream which was very much swollen, and there was no bridge and no plank to cross it. Then the bride nimbly took her clothes up, and wanted to wade through it. And just as she was thus standing in the water a man – and it was the enchanter – cried mockingly close beside her, "Aha! Where are thine eyes that thou takest that for water?"

Then her eyes were opened, and she saw that she was standing with her clothes lifted up in the middle of a field that was blue with flowers of blue flax. All the people saw it likewise, and chased her away with ridicule and laughter.

Jacob Ludwig Grimm and Wilhelm Carl Grimm

- Write brief notes about the comparisons.

	Grimm's Beam	Other fairy tales
Language and style		
Settings		
Types of plot		
Types of character		

Dear Helper,

Objective: to read a fairy tale and compare it with other known fairy tales.

Fairy tales have distinctive features which make them recognisable from other types of story. Help your child to identify those features and also to see how this fairy tale compares with others.

Night Clouds

- Make brief notes on the figurative language in this poem. The first line has been done as an example.

Night Clouds	Notes on figurative language
The white mares of the moon rush along the sky	The clouds look like white horses rushing across the sky.
Beating their golden hoofs upon the glass Heavens;	
The white mares of the moon are all standing on their hind legs	
Pawing at the green porcelain doors of the remotest Heavens.	
Fly, mares!	
Strain your utmost,	
Scatter the milky dust of stars,	
Or the tiger sun will leap upon you and destroy you	
With one lick of his vermillion tongue.	
by Amy Lowell	

Dear Helper,

Objective: to make notes about a poem in response to a specific question.

Figurative language is simply 'picture language'. A writer gives a picture or image to describe something more clearly, eg *his feet were as cold as an iceberg*. The two commonest figures of speech are similes and metaphors. A *simile* is a comparison using 'like' or 'as' (the above example is a simile); a *metaphor* is a direct comparison, eg *his feet were icebergs*.

Housecarle

- Write a short summary (approximately 100 words) of this passage.

Earl Sigurd's arms ached with the weight of the battle-axe which he had wielded all day. There was little force left in his blows now, and each Norman attack seemed fiercer than the last. But the line held, the unbreakable line of housecarles[1] that defended King Harold on Senlac Hill.

Arrows! Earl Sigurd swung his shield from his left shoulder and held it high, letting his battle-axe hang loosely in his right hand. The arrows fell as thick as a rainstorm but glanced harmlessly off his shield. Then came the onslaught – huge war-horses lumbered slowly up the rising ground under the weight of hauberk-clad[2] knights. Sigurd slung his shield over his shoulder so that he could raise his axe with both hands. Wait – wait for the right moment – and swing. Swing at a horse's chest or a knight's leg and try not to be sickened by the gushing blood or the screams of agony. Concentrate on parrying the next lance thrust, then swing again. Ignore the sickness in the gut and the searing pain in the muscles. In a moment the tide will turn, giving a merciful breathing space before the next onslaught.

Again the arrows! Mechanically Sigurd reached for his shield. But this time something was different. Something had broken the relentless rhythm of the battle. Housecarles were turning their backs on the Norman knights and rushing towards the dragon standard of Wessex where a voice was screaming, ringing above all the other screams of battle. All at once Sigurd knew. Knew even before he heard the word – King Harold had fallen, and with him their last hope. But there was no time to think of what that meant. A mounted knight loomed above him swinging a huge broadsword. Sigurd heaved his axe, but he was too slow, too late, too tired, and before he could strike, the sword smashed down on his helmet bringing sudden hot pain, then blackness.

He awoke to a splitting headache, silence and darkness.

"Where am I?" he groaned. He heard a movement as a candle was lit. At first the light hurt his eyes, but as he got used to it he saw that he was in a humble peasant's cottage.

"We are at Tonbridge, twenty miles north of Hastings." It was Oswulf, one of his thanes.

"And the battle?"

"Lost, and the King dead!"

[1] *housecarles:* member of King's bodyguard.
[2] *hauberk:* knee-length protective garment made of metal rings.

Dear Helper,

Objective: to write a summary of part of a book.
Read the passage with your child. Before writing anything, ask them to summarise it orally. Then, discuss how the summary might be improved to capture just the main ideas and the important names, places and dates.

Name:

Design a book jacket

- Use this model to produce a book jacket. Make brief notes in the table below.

Information about the author	Write a 'blurb' for the book, saying what can be found inside. If the book is a novel, this could be a summary of the story – BUT DON'T GIVE AWAY THE ENDING! Price ISBN (book number) and barcode.	Title Author Publisher	**TITLE** Author Publisher	Information about the author
BACK FLAP	BACK COVER	SPINE	FRONT COVER	FRONT FLAP

Front flap Information about the book.	
Front cover Title, author, publisher, idea for illustration or photograph.	
Spine Title, author and publisher.	
Back cover Notes for the back cover blurb.	
Back flap Information about the author.	

Dear Helper,

Objective: to design a book jacket that includes a blurb.

One of the challenges of this activity is to make the information about the book on the front flap different from that on the back cover blurb. The former should be an objective description, while the blurb should entice the prospective reader into buying and reading the book.

Book-o-meter

- Write a review of a book by filling in the 'read outs' on the book-o-meter.

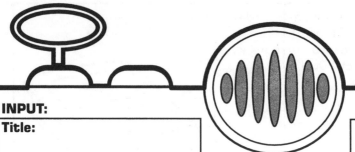

INPUT:
Title:

INPUT:
Author:

Screen 1: Main Character
Description:

Screen 2: Setting
Description:

Screen 3: Best scene
Describe the most exciting screen:

THE METER:
Draw in the needle.

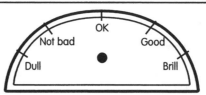

OK
Not bad   Good
Dull   Brill

Say what you liked/disliked:

Dear Helper,

Objective: to write a book review for children of the same age.

Encourage your child to talk to you about the book they are reviewing before they write down their responses on the sheet.

Skylark

- Compare these two texts about skylarks. Think about these questions:
  What is the purpose of each text?
  What differences can you see in the layout of the words?
  What differences are there in the language?
  Which text gives the most accurate information about the Skylark?
  Which did you most enjoy?

- Write your answers on the back of the sheet or on a separate piece of paper.

Skylark

You are most likely to hear a Skylark rather than see it. It sings as it rises high in the sky, circles and hovers over its nest. The Skylark's speckled brown feathers make it hard to see against the open ground, but in winter you may see flocks feeding on seeds, worms and insects. Look then for the small crest on top of their heads. The Skylark builds a nest of grass on the ground and lays three to five eggs. In parts of Europe, Skylarks are still shot and eaten as a delicacy.

Family group: Lark
Size: Up to 18cm
Call: Loud, clear, warbling song

The Ecstatic

Lark, skylark, spilling your rubbed and round
Pebbles of sound in air's still lake,
Whose widening circles fill the noon: yet none
Is known so small beside the sun:

Be strong your fervent soaring, your skyward air!
Tremble there, a nerve of song!
Float up there where voice and wing are one,
A singing star, a note of fight!

Buoyed, embayed in heaven's noon – wide reaches –
For soon light's tide will turn – oh stay!
Cease not till day streams to the west, then down
That estuary drop down to peace.

C Day Lewis

Dear Helper,

Objective: to compare different texts.

This activity is designed to help your child develop an understanding of different types of writing. The writers of each of these pieces had different intentions in writing them. Ask your child: *What was the writer's intention in each case?*

Fairy tale cards 1: Meetings

Imagine you meet

A talking toad

Imagine you meet

A wicked sorceror

Imagine you meet

A beautiful princess /handsome prince

Imagine you meet

A giant

Imagine you meet

A dragon

Imagine you meet

A lost child

Imagine you meet

An armoured knight

Imagine you meet

A wise old woman

Imagine you meet

A goblin

- Use these cards with 'Fairy tale cards 2' to write a fairy tale. Shuffle the two packs ('Meetings' and 'Finds') and select one card from each pack.
- Make up a story around the two cards.
- Tell the story to a friend or relative, then write it down. Tell the story in the first person ('I'). Extend the story, if you wish, by choosing another 'Meetings' card.

Dear Helper,

Objective: to write an extended story.

First encourage your child to tell you a story. Then, ask questions to stimulate further ideas before your child writes the story down.

Fairy tale cards 2: Finds

Imagine you find — **A magic lamp**

Imagine you find — **A bag of gold**

Imagine you find — **A treasure map**

Imagine you find — **A cloak of invisibility**

Imagine you find — **A magic carpet**

Imagine you find — **A potion for eternal life**

Imagine you find — **A book of spells**

Imagine you find — **A crown**

Imagine you find — **A crystal ball**

- Use these cards with 'Fairy tale cards 1' to write a fairy tale. Shuffle the two packs ('Meetings' and 'Finds') and select one card from each pack.
- Make up a story around the two cards.
- Tell the story to a friend or relative, then write it down. Tell the story in the first person ('I'). Extend the story, if you wish, by choosing another 'Meetings' card.

Dear Helper,

Objective: to write an extended story.
First encourage your child to tell you a story. Then, ask questions to stimulate further ideas before your child writes the story down.

Name:

Spiders

- Skim the text (one minute) to find five key points about spiders. Highlight them.
- Scan the text to find out whether the Tarantula or the Black Widow is the more dangerous.
- Make a glossary of the technical terms in the text.

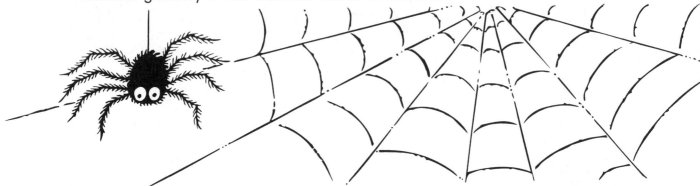

The word spider comes from the Anglo-Saxon word *spinnan*, meaning 'to spin'. Spiders vary in length from less than 0.1 centimetre to more than 10 centimetres. They have two body parts and eight legs. Each leg has seven segments, and on the tip of the legs are two tiny claws.

Like insects, spiders have a hard body shell called an 'exoskeleton'. They also have an internal skeleton that serves as a surface for muscle attachment. Spiders have no antennae. They do, however, have two structures called 'pedipalps', which they use to handle their prey while feeding.

Spiders have as many as eight simple eyes, but their eyesight is not as well developed as that of insects. Instead, the world of spiders is one of vibrations that are sensed through the surface on which the spider lives. All spiders' activities, including feeding, mating and egg-laying, take place while they are suspended from silk threads.

Spiders are the only animals that digest their food outside their bodies. After their prey is captured, spiders expel digestive enzymes onto the victim. The enzymes break down its body tissues and, after a few seconds, the spider sucks up the predigested, liquid tissues. By repeating this process many times, spiders digest the entire animal.

One of the most notable things about spiders is their ability to spin silk. Spider silk is a remarkable material which can make nets strong enough to withstand the impact of fast-flying insects. Some spiders spin silks that are stronger than steel piano wire. All spiders have silk glands and spinning organs called spinnerets.

Most spiders are harmless to humans, but a few species are responsible for the fear which many people feel for spiders. The Tarantula is a huge hairy spider that looks really frightening. It spins no web, but relies on speed to catch its prey. Its bite is poisonous but is rarely fatal. The Black Widow is smaller than the Tarantula, but is much more dangerous as it is one of the few spiders whose bite can be fatal to humans.

Dear Helper,

Objective: to find information by skimming and scanning a text.

Remind your child that *skimming* is skipping over the text quickly, looking for key words and phrases. When a key word or phrase has been found, the eye *scans* along the lines of text to see if it is relevant. If so, that section of text is read normally and the required information is noted.

Cor!

- Divide this story into paragraphs by writing a paragraph marker **//** where each new paragraph should begin.
  Clue: Look for steps forward in time, eg 'next day'.

There was once a spider called Humphrey who lived in a dark hole in the bottom of the Richards' cellar. Every day Lucy Richards came down to play and to feed her guinea pigs. Humphrey envied them so much because they got lots of love and attention. One day he decided that he would show himself in the hope that Lucy would love him and play with him. So that day, just as she was putting her guinea pigs away, he crept out from his dark hole. But when Lucy saw him she screamed with fright. Humphrey was so upset that he crawled back in his hole and sulked for a long time. Next day, he went for a walk around the cellar trying to find something to make him more beautiful. He found an old, cracked mirror and took a good look at himself. He couldn't see what Lucy had been so frightened of. He had a lovely hairy coat and nice bristly legs. He was just about to crawl back to his hole when he saw an old make-up bag. It had soap, shampoo, perfume and lipstick inside it. He washed all eight legs, shampooed his bristly coat, sprinkled perfume all over and put some lipstick on. Then he went to look in the mirror again. He looked so handsome that he felt sure Lucy would like him better than her guinea pigs. Later on that day Lucy came downstairs again. Humphrey walked out very proudly and smiled at her with his bright red lips. She screamed even more loudly than before. After that, poor Humphrey was so sad he decided that he was going to drown himself, so he walked towards the sink very slowly with his head down. When he passed the washing machine he heard a voice. 'Cor!' it said. When he looked round he saw a lovely black silky female spider. When Humphrey got home, he decided to find out more about female spiders from an old encyclopedia. He was horrified when he found out that, after mating, the female spider eats the male. Humphrey decided that he would not ask the female spider for a date after all. But whenever he felt unloved all he had to do was walk past the washing machine and he would hear a voice saying 'Cor!' and that really cheered him up.

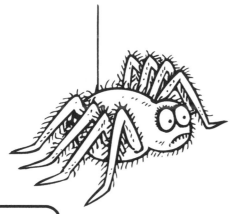
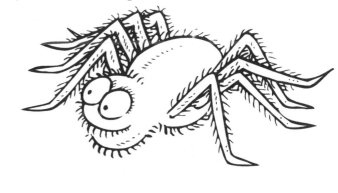

Dear Helper,

Objective: to divide a story into paragraphs.
Remind your child that paragraphs break up big chunks of text to make it easier to read and understand. New paragraphs might start when: 1) something new happens; 2) a new person is introduced; 3) there is a change of time or place; 4) someone new speaks.

Euthanasia

- Divide this argumentative text into paragraphs by writing a paragraph marker // where each new paragraph should begin.
  Clue: Look for each new argument.

Is euthanasia justified?

Euthanasia means mercy killing. It means ending a life so as to release a person from an incurable disease or great pain. Voluntary euthanasia is a request for death by the patient or a representative. Passive euthanasia means allowing someone to die; active euthanasia involves taking deliberate action to cause death. Christians, Jews and Muslims all believe that human life is sacred and condemn euthanasia in any form. As Western laws are based on the views of these religions, most countries consider the act of helping someone to die to be a form of murder, punishable by law. Even withholding help to prevent death has frequently been severely punished. On the other hand, some doctors, such as Dr Kevorkian from the United States, believe that terminally ill, or seriously disabled, patients have "a right to die". They are often in great pain, and all that doctors achieve by keeping them alive is to drag out their pain and suffering. Dr Kevorkian is believed to have helped over 100 patients to die, and was convicted and served a prison sentence for these acts. Society would call these acts "crimes", whereas he believed that they were acts of mercy. However, a person like Stephen Hawking, the famous British scientist, is a powerful argument against euthanasia. He was born with such serious deformities that some people might have thought his life was not worth living. His motor neurone disease means that he has hardly any control over his body. He communicates through an electronic voice box, and moves around using an electronically controlled wheelchair which he can operate with slight movements of his thumbs. Yet he has led a very productive life and made a great scientific contribution in the field of cosmology, popularising the subject through his best-seller *A Brief History of Time*. Another argument against euthanasia is the fear that it may be used wrongly. An example is the euthanasia committees in Nazi Germany that were empowered to condemn and execute anyone found to be a burden to the state. Old people would be particularly vulnerable to this kind of misuse. Perhaps the most powerful argument against euthanasia is ethical, whether this is from a religious or a humanist point of view. We did not make human life, so it is wrong that we should take it away. No human being should be able to decide about the life and death of another human being.

Dear Helper,

Objective: to divide an argumentative text into paragraphs.

Remind your child that paragraphs break up big chunks of text to make it easier to read and understand. The start of new paragraphs for this kind of writing might be for: 1) the introduction; 2) a new argument; 3) a counter argument; 4) an extended example; 5) the conclusion.

Form finder

- Choose a **subject** to write about, then roll two dice (or one, twice) to randomly select a **form**, a **purpose** and an **audience**. Do this several times until you find a combination that interests or excites you.

- Write about the subject using the form you have chosen for the purpose and audience you have chosen.

	Subject	Form	Purpose	Audience
2	cloning	encyclopaedia entry	to inform	your own age group
3	ghosts	instruction manual	to explain	young children
4	an animal	letter	to remind	an expert in the subject
5	losing something	newspaper article	to express your feelings	old people
6	school dinners	play	to educate	the general public
7	love	poem	to express your opinion	someone who knows nothing about it
8	computers	reference book chapter	to describe	your teacher
9	a piece of music	report	to persuade	your best friend
10	a holiday	series of diary entries	to entertain	yourself
11	a problem	story	to complain	adults
12	your own choice	musical	to impress	people who are not interested

Dear Helper,

Objective: to write appropriately in a chosen form for a specific purpose and audience.

Remind your child that if writers are to succeed in getting their ideas across, they have to be clear about their purpose, audience, and the most suitable form for the subject. Make sure your child has generated a series of choices which are easy to write about.

PHOTOCOPIABLE

Name _____

Year 6 Homework Diary

Name of activity	Date sent home	Child's comments		Helper's comments	Teacher's comments
		Did you like this? ☑ Tick a face.	**Write some comments on what you learned.**		
		☺ a lot 😐 a little ☹ not much			
		☺ a lot 😐 a little ☹ not much			
		☺ a lot 😐 a little ☹ not much			
		☺ a lot 😐 a little ☹ not much			